Jonathan Goodman has been described by Julian Symons as 'the premier investigator of crimes past'. He was editor of the Celebrated Trials series and has written a number of books on crime including *Murder in High Places* and *Murder in Low Places*.

Jonathan Goodman is a member of the Medico-legal Society and is one of the few lay members of the British Academy of Forensic Sciences.

Also by Jonathan Goodman

THE RAILWAY MURDERS
THE PLEASURES OF MURDER
THE SEASIDE MURDERS
THE COUNTRY HOUSE MURDERS
THE ART OF MURDER
THE LADY KILLERS

The Medical Murders

Edited by
JONATHAN GOODMAN

WARNER BOOKS

A WARNER BOOK

First published in Great Britain in 1991
by Judy Piatkus (Publishers) Ltd
Published in 1992 by Warner Books

A CIP catalogue record for this book
is available from the British Library.

ISBN 0 7515 0002 X

Printed in England by Clays Ltd, St Ives plc

Warner Books
A Division of
Little, Brown and Company (UK) Limited
165 Great Dover Street
London SE1 4YA

For members of
The Organon Club,
particularly these doctors:
David Foster, Lewis Gavin, Sir Montague Levine
and Professor James Payne

Contents

Deadly Remedies

WHILE SHERLOCK HOLMES was investigating the case that Dr Watson, afterwards chronicling it, called *The Adventure of the Speckled Band*, he asserted: 'When a doctor does go wrong, he is the first of criminals. He has nerve and he has knowledge....' Then, perhaps in retrospective observance of his dictum that 'it is a capital mistake to theorise before one has data,' Holmes added: 'Palmer and Pritchard were among the heads of their profession' – a statement that, as readers of this anthology will learn if they didn't know it already, considerably overstated the professional prestige of those medical unworthies.

The addendum apart, Holmes's assertion makes sense. Doctors do have nerve (speaking of present-day private ones, the nerve, bordering on cheek, to charge almost as much per-minute as lawyers and motor-mechanics do). They have knowledge – of, probably for instance, toxicology and anatomy: knowledge which many lay premedicating murderers will envy. And, apropos of premeditated murders, doctors have the wonderful blessing of being able to certify unnatural deaths as natural – which, more than all other criminous abilities put together, helps make the truly *'perfect* murder', that being of the kind that no one knows has been committed.

The medical murderers gathered herein (eleven doctors, a dentist, and a non-registered nurse) only exemplify the species. I suppose the most conspicuous absentees are

1

Messrs Burke & Hare, both come from Ireland and singularly forenamed William, makers of corpses by appointment to Dr Robert Knox's school of practical anatomy in Surgeons' Square, Edinburgh, in 1828: Jacques Barzun's account of their partnership is among *The Pleasures of Murder*, which, not intended to have company, turned out to be the sparking volumes of this series of anthologies (and I too have written about Burke & Hare − and the subsequently similarly motivated Londoners, Bishop, Williams & May − for a book called *Murder in Low Places*, first published in England by the original publishers of this one).

A shame, because he really should be here, but I have not come across a decent article about Carl Coppolino, the American anaesthetist who, in the late 1960s, was tried, then tried again, that time successfully, for a murder with the aid of a hypnotic drug lengthily entitled succinyl-choline chloride. In a way conversely, I have left out the American Dr Hawley Harvey Crippen (hanged in London in 1910, having been brought back here from Canada, for the murder of his wife with the aid of a hypnotic drug, the name of which, hyoscine, looks like a dyslexic version of the name of the flower that sprang from the blood of Hyacinthus, the youth unintentionally killed by Apollo, patron of, among other things, medicine) because, so it seems to me, there are more than enough accounts of the Crippen case in books presently in print.

I might, just might, have considered Dr Edward Seys Massiah as a candidate for this collection were it not that the evidence suggesting, no more than suggesting, that he was responsible for one of the two simultaneous but separate Brighton Trunk Crimes of 1934 is given in the essay on both of them that is my main overt contribution to *The Railway Murders*.

Speaking of Brighton reminds me to mention that John Bodkin Adams, lately of nearby Eastbourne, is, no doubt disappointingly to some readers, missing from this collection − for the simple reason that he does not deserve inclusion. English defending barristers are rarely able to pull off Perry-Masonesque tricks in court; and when they do, it is usually because the prosecution, made lackadaisical by excessive confidence, has not bothered to rummage within its metaphorical Crown for the presence of figurative rabbits that, having cheerfully chewed chunks from the sham-silk lining, are sleeping snug till defence counsel decides that the time is dramatically right to pull them out by their handy ears. That was so in the spring of 1957, when Dr Adams was tried at the Old Bailey for the murder of a patient who had remembered him in her penultimate will: his counsel, wonderfully untriumphant, produced written records that flatly contradicted the spoken testimony of the doctor's crucial accusers, itinerant nurses who had not let facts interfere with their tittle-tattled suspicions that the doctor had not administered morphine mercifully, 'to ease the passing of a dying person', but murderously. He was acquitted (but was later found guilty of, and fined for, forgery of certain prescriptions, an offence which also resulted in his being struck off the Medical Register; reinstated in the early 1960s, he resumed his practice in Eastbourne, and was always well stocked with patients, some of them wealthy widows who willed him remembrances, till he himself died in 1984, leaving more than eighty-three-year-old GPs usually do).

The acquittal at the murder trial was proper: there was no scintilla of *evidence* that anyone had been murdered, let alone of evidence that the defendant had maliciously, from greed, eased any of his patients' passings. Those negative facts were imparted by Dr Adams's solicitor to Penguin Books when, a few years after the trial, they published a paperback edition of Sybille Bedford's report of the proceedings, carefully called *The Best We Can Do*. Uniquely, so far as I know, the solicitor alleged libel on a coloured ground. In those days, Penguin put far more emphasis than they do these days on 'genre colours', an orange jacket signifying straight fiction, blue being used for non-fiction, reference works having black jackets, and so on. Dr Adams's solicitor told Penguin that his client was dismayed that they had dressed *The Best We Can Do* in a green jacket — for in the Penguin spectrum, green stood for crime. Dr Adams had been acquitted, which in the circumstances of the trial for murder, meant that the jury considered that no crime had been committed. By jacketing in green, Penguin — so the lawyer contended — were, in unambiguous effect, saying that the verdict was wrong: that a crime *had* been committed: that the doctor, he alone suspected of the alleged crime, had got away with murder.

Since I don't want to run the slightest risk of writing something that upsets any of the surviving interested parties, I shall merely note that the green-jacketed *The Best We Can Do* was not withdrawn from sale, and say no more.

Jonathan Goodman
London, 1990

The Jigsaw Murder Case

JONATHAN GOODMAN

IF YOU ARE old enough to remember the first croonings of a romantic song, 'Red Sails in the Sunset'— which, had there been such a thing as a pop chart in the mid-1930s, would have been top of it for a good many weeks — you may also recall an illicit version of the lyric which went like this:

> Red stains on the carpet,
> Red stains on your knife,
> Oh, Dr Buck Ruxton, you cut up your wife;
> The nursemaid, she saw you, and threatened to tell —
> So, Dr Buck Ruxton, you killed her as well.

The fact that this anonymous rhyme was recited and sung on innumerable occasions gives an idea of the interest and excitement caused by a double murder in a small northern county town.

So far as public awareness is concerned, the case began on the bright but chilly afternoon of Sunday, 29 September 1935, when Susan Johnson, a young Edinburgh woman holidaying with her brother at Moffatt, a picturesque village thirty-five or so miles across the Scottish border from Carlisle, took a stroll to the bridge over Gardenholme Linn, a stream running into the River Annan.
  Glancing over the rough stone parapet, she saw....
  No, it couldn't possibly be.
  She looked again. Her heart was thumping by now.

5

The second look convinced her that she was staring at a human arm, protruding from some wrapping at the side of the ravine.

Susan Johnson rushed back to the hotel. When she told her brother Alfred why she was in such a state, he asked the landlord to give her some medicinal whisky, then raced to the bridge. Clambering down the heather-strewn embankment, he saw not only an arm just above the water-line, some ten yards from the bridge, but an oddly-shaped bundle wrapped in bed-sheeting and newspaper.

He timorously pulled apart the wrapping and saw that the parcel contained chunks of flesh and bone.

Deciding that he had seen enough – more than enough – Alfred went in search of the village policeman and told him how the beauty of Gardenholme Linn had been marred.

After confirming that this was no false alarm, Constable James Fairweather telephoned the headquarters of the Dumfriesshire Constabulary, then went back to the bridge. And waited.

Not for long. Dumfries is no more than twenty miles from Moffatt, and Sergeant Robert Sloan rarely needed to slow down on the gently curving road that Sunday afternoon.

One wonders what went through his mind as he drove. Did he perhaps think about the Brighton Trunk Crimes that had caused such a stir the year before? Did he fear that something similar – parcelled remains rather than bodies as luggage – would create as much work, as many problems, for himself and his colleagues?

He parked near the bridge, and had a few words with Constable Fairweather and Alfred Johnson; then treading carefully so as not to disturb the ground, he lowered himself down the side of the gully.

Within a few minutes, he had observed four parcels. After an hour, he had carefully parted the paper and sheeting and made a rough inventory of the respective contents, which included parts of legs, hands (with the tips of fingers and thumbs lopped off), thigh-bones, miscellaneous pieces of flesh, the chest portion of a human trunk, and two heads, hideously mutilated so as to be unrecognisable.

By the time Sloan had completed his notes and marked the positions of the parcels, other policemen had arrived from Dumfries. It was starting to get dark. Constable Fairweather unlocked the diminutive mortuary in Moffatt Cemetery, and the parcels were transported there.

During the next few days, forensic experts from Edinburgh and Glasgow visited the mortuary and made preliminary examinations of the decomposing, maggoty remains. One of the experts was John Glaister, who had been appointed Professor of Forensic Medicine at the University of Glasgow four years before, following the retirement of his famous father.

Then the 'bits and pieces,' as John Glaister referred to the remains, were taken to the anatomy department at Edinburgh University. Between the time of their arrival there and 4 November, they were augmented by the contents of other parcels found by the police and the public close to Gardenholme Linn and along the River Annan. The parcel farthest removed from those that had started the investigation was discovered at Johnson Bridge, on the main Edinburgh-Carlisle road, nine miles from Moffatt.

The malformed, 'Cyclops' eye of an animal was found among the remains. It was better preserved than the human flesh and tissues, suggesting that it had been immersed in formaldehyde, perhaps by someone interested in ophthalmology.

While the pathologists, an anatomist and a dentist tried to solve the two 'jigsaw puzzles', and to find distinguishing marks to assist in identifying the victims, the police made inquiries about persons reported missing before 19 September, when there had been torrential rain in the area around Moffatt, filling streams and rivers; it seemed clear that the parcels had been left behind on the banks as the level of the water had fallen.

Medical Murders

The police had one apparently important clue. A piece of newspaper that had helped to wrap one of the packages was recognised as being part of the *Sunday Graphic* of 15 September 1935: part of a special 'slip' edition of 3700 copies, carrying a report and pictures of the crowning of the Morecambe Carnival Queen, that had been distributed only around Morecambe and the nearby county town of Lancaster.

On the very same day that the Chief Constable of Dumfries got in touch with the Lancaster police, he happened to notice a report in the *Glasgow Daily Record*. Briefly tucked away on an inside page, the report referred to the disappearance, in mid-September, of Mary Jane Rogerson, the twenty-year-old nursemaid to the children of an Indian doctor named Buck Ruxton, who ministered to the sick at his home at 2 Dalton Square, Lancaster, one hundred and five miles south of the bridge over Gardenholme Linn.

Struck by the Lancasterian coincidence, the Chief Constable initiated inquiries in that town. He soon learned that the disappearance of Mary Rogerson had been notified to the local police — also that there was a rumour that Dr Ruxton's wife had left him at about the time the nursemaid was last seen.

A detective was sent to get a detailed description of the missing girl from her step-mother, who lived in Morecambe, and as a result of the visit two further pieces of information came to light.

The human remains found at and near Moffatt had been wrapped mainly in newspaper and bed-linen — but a blouse and a child's romper suit had also been used. When the blouse was shown to Mrs Rogerson, she at once recognised it, saying that she had bought it at a jumble sale and given it to Mary just before Christmas 1934; she had no doubt that it was the same blouse, for she had sewn a patch under one of the arms.

Mrs Rogerson told the police that, during the summer, her step-daughter and two of the Ruxtons' three children

8

had spent a fortnight in a guesthouse at Grange-over-Sands, and that the landlady had given Mary some secondhand clothes.

A detective visited the landlady, Mrs Edith Holme, who instantly identified the romper suit as one of the things she had given the nursemaid: her own child had outgrown the suit; before parting with it, she had put new elastic in the waistband, tying the ends in a knot of her invention.

So far, the control and conduct of the investigation had been emphatically Scottish; but now, although the scientific work of piecing together the assortment of human remains continued in Edinburgh, overall responsibility for the case was passed to Captain Henry Vann, the Chief Constable of Lancaster.

Captain Vann and his subordinates already knew quite a lot about Dr Buck Ruxton — and in a few days, without having to put themselves out to any great extent, they learned much more.

When Ruxton was born in Bombay, in 1899, he was called Bukhtar Rustomji Ratanji Hakim, or Buck Hakim for short, but some thirty years later he anglicised his name by deed poll.

He was touchy about being referred to simply as an Indian, and would insist on the more specific designation of Parsee, pointing out that he was a descendant of the Zoroastrians who migrated from Persia to India in the eighth century.

He held three medical degrees, two from the University of Bombay and one (MB) from the University of London.

After gaining the first of those degrees, he served for about three years in the Indian Medical Corps and then travelled to Britain, where he lived first of all in London, working as a locum while pursuing his studies, and then in Edinburgh, preparing for the examinations for Fellowship of the Royal College of Surgeons of that city.

His failure in that examination may been due, at least in part, to the fact that his dedication to his studies was diminished by his infatuation for Isabella Van Ess, a woman two years younger than himself who, following her estrangement from her Dutch husband, was working as a waitress in a restaurant in Princes Street, Edinburgh.

Sharp-nosed, wide-mouthed, and with legs that did not narrow towards the ankles, Isabella was far less lovely than her name; but still, Ruxton was smitten from the moment she first took an order from him for tea and scones.

Presumably because he decided that Isabella would consider him more dashing if she thought he was an army officer, decently reticent about his many decorations for gallantry, he led her to believe that he was Captain Hakim.

He returned to London at the beginning of 1928, and Isabella joined him soon afterwards. Though she was now divorced, and though between 1929 and 1933 she gave birth to three children, she never married Ruxton.

In 1930, Dr and 'Mrs' Ruxton, with their first child, Elizabeth, moved to 2 Dalton Square, a grey-stone terrace house of three storeys and a basement that stood next to a picture palace in the centre of Lancaster. Of the four rooms on the ground floor, two each side of a hall, Ruxton used three for his general medical practice, one as a waiting room, one for consultations, the third as a surgery; the fourth room, at the back, was a kitchen.

There were two living rooms and a dining room on the first floor, and at some time since the house had been built, towards the end of the nineteenth century, a bathroom had been squeezed in as a sort of addition to the first-floor landing. There was a master bedroom and three smaller ones on the top floor.

Ruxton soon had a large panel of patients. This was partly due to an insufficiency of doctors in the town, partly because his practice was very general indeed, including even dentistry and ophthalmology, and partly because he seemed invariably affable, worthy of the locals' descriptions of him as 'that nice, obliging, young foreign doctor'.

But Isabella did not consider him altogether nice. As the months, the years, went by, the couple quarrelled with increasing frequency and vehemence.

Sometimes the rows were over what Ruxton called 'Belle's temporary sillinesses'. Sometimes the cause was jealousy: Ruxton was particularly suspicious of a friend of Isabella's, a young man called Bobby Edmondson who worked in the solicitor's department at the town hall, just across the square from the doctor's house. And sometimes there was a sexual motive for the arguments, for both Ruxton and Isabella experienced enhanced pleasure from intimacy when it was part of 'making-up'.

By April 1935, Isabella was either tired of Ruxton's tantrums or terrified by his bad temper. As the result of a statement she made to a detective, Ruxton was invited to the police station. When he saw his 'wife' there, he (in the detective's words) 'flew into a violent passion and said, "My wife has been unfaithful. I would be justified in murdering her".'

The detective pacified Ruxton (or thought so), reassured Isabella (or believed that he had), and put the incident out of his mind – until a month or so later, when he was called to 2 Dalton Square, again to act as peace-maker.

It would have been better for Isabella – and for the young nursemaid, Mary Rogerson – if, instead of seeking help from the police, she had waited until Buck Ruxton was answering a house-call and then escaped to a place where he might not find her or could not harm her.

Following the press reports of the gruesome discoveries at Moffatt – and long before the police suspected Ruxton of murder – a good many people in Lancaster, including the doctor's several charwomen and some of his patients and neighbours, wondered whether there was a connection between what they had read in the papers and the disappearance of Mrs Ruxton and the nursemaid.

Both before and after the mutilated remains were found, Ruxton contended on various occasions and to various people that the two women had gone to Blackpool ... that they were taking a holiday in Scotland ... that the nursemaid was pregnant, so Isabella might have taken her

11

away for an abortion ... that Isabella had gone off with a lover ... that she had returned to London.

When early newspaper accounts stated (wrongly, as it turned out) that some of the remains found at Moffatt were of a man, Ruxton was joyful. After giving one of the charwomen a rest from her chores while he read aloud a report of the 'Ravine Murder,' he chortled, 'So you see, Mrs Oxley, it is a man and a woman – not our two,' then burst into helpless laughter at Mrs Oxley's response that she sincerely hoped not.

But within a week of that incident he was distinctly unhappy about what the papers were saying. He turned up at the police station at half-past nine on the night of Friday, 11 October, and, waving a copy of the *Daily Express* in one hand and furiously gesticulating with the other, screamed at the Chief Constable that such publicity was ruining his practice.

While Captain Vann tried to get a word in edgeways, Ruxton sat on the desk, perched his feet on a visitor's chair, and banged the back of it with his free hand.

Abruptly changing the subject – and crying now – Ruxton accused a man of being Isabella's lover, claimed that he had tapped telephone conversations between them, and implored Captain Vann to intercept the alleged lover's mail.

Then, reverting to the press, he asked the Chief Constable to issue a statement that the remains found in and around Moffatt were not those of Isabella and Mary Rogerson. Captain Vann was still uming and ahing about that when the doctor stalked out.

Uming and ahing. . .? Well, yes. If only because Ruxton's arrival had interrupted a discussion between Captain Vann and a senior detective as to whether the time was ripe to charge the doctor with double murder.

Ever since the responsibility for the investigation had been passed to Lancaster from Dumfriesshire, the Lancaster Borough Police Force had been just as busy as the scientists gathered in the anatomy department at Edinburgh

University, piecing together the incomplete jigsaws of flesh and bone, and drawing conclusions from what they found — and could not find.

The police knew, among many other things, that on Saturday, 14 September, Mrs Ruxton had driven to Blackpool in the doctor's Hillman car, registration number CP 8415, to see the illuminations with her two sisters, and that she had started the return journey just before midnight. Though she was never seen alive again, the presence of the car in Lancaster the next day indicated that she had arrived home.

Some of the strongest evidence against Ruxton came from his charwomen. At half-past six on the morning of Sunday, 15 September, Mrs Agnes Oxley was getting ready to go to the doctor's house when Ruxton drove up in his car and told her that she could have the day off as 'Mrs Ruxton and Mary have gone away on a holiday to Edinburgh'.

That afternoon, however, the doctor visited one of his patients, Mrs Mary Hampshire, and asked if she wanted to earn seven shillings and sixpence by scrubbing his staircase. He explained that he needed her help because Isabella was in Blackpool and Mary Rogerson in Edinburgh, and he had cut his hand badly in trying to open a tin of peaches for the children's breakfast. (He certainly had a severe wound on one of his fingers, and a subsequent remark to Mrs Hampshire that he had taken his children to stay with a dentist friend in Morecambe was true.)

When Mrs Hampshire arrived at 2 Dalton Square, she found that the place was far more messy and untidy than she had expected: the carpets had been taken from the stairs, which were scattered with straw; rolled-up carpets, stair-pads and a man's suit were lying in the waiting room, and in the back yard were other carpets, clothing and towels, all heavily stained with blood and showing signs that an attempt had been made to burn them.

Mrs Hampshire, a trusting soul, accepted the doctor's explanation that the carpets had been taken up because the house was to be decorated, and seems to have assumed that, though Ruxton did not look anaemic, the blood saturating the things in the yard had flowed from the cut on his finger.

She did not ask him to explain the straw protruding from beneath the doors to two of the bedrooms — or why those doors were locked and the keys removed.

Mrs Hampshire started tidying up, and, when her husband came to the house a few hours later, got him to lend a hand. Ruxton gave the couple a load of soiled carpets and clothing, but presumably Mrs Hampshire was paid more than the promised seven shillings and sixpence for her labours, not only on the Sunday but on subsequent days, on some of which she was assisted by the doctor's regular chars.

The police had much more evidence against Ruxton, including the testimony of a cyclist who on Tuesday, 17 September, had been knocked over by the doctor's car on a road leading to Moffatt; Ruxton had not stopped but was caught by a policeman, who noted that he was as jumpy as a flea.

But all this evidence might be insufficient to convict Buck Ruxton if the scientists in Edinburgh were unable to establish that the bits and pieces of flesh and bone on their laboratory tables were the remains of Isabella Ruxton and Mary Rogerson.

It was vital that the separated, mutilated remains found in Dumfriesshire be identified as those of the doctor's common-law wife and his children's nursemaid. Admittedly, by the time of the Ruxton case there can have been few judges who wholly accepted Lord Halsbury's contention that 'in the absence of evidence (that a body or part of a body has been found, which is proved to be that of the person alleged to have been killed) there is no onus upon the prisoner to account for the disappearance or nonproduction of the person'.

Only the year before, a man named Davidson had been

convicted of the murder of his small son though no body had been found, the presumption being that the body was consumed in a fire on a garbage tip.

But a clever defence lawyer might confuse less clever members of a jury about the meaning of 'reasonable doubt' by speaking of ancient cases in which men had been hanged for the murder of people who had afterwards, like Mark Twain, complained of reports of their demise, and use any uncertainty concerning the fact of death to suggest uncertainty about the act of murder.

The team of experts at Edinburgh University not only used accepted methods but invented new techniques as they sorted out which of the remains belonged to one body, which to the other — as they then searched for clues that might, singly or in relation to others, give more reality to the incomplete bodies than the original designations of 'No 1' and 'No 2' — as they sought indications of the cause, or causes of death.

Probably for the first time, an anatomist had been brought into a murder investigation. This was James Couper Brash, professor of anatomy at the University of Edinburgh — a city that, a hundred or so years before, had become associated, through the activities of Burke and Hare, with the unlawful aspects of the science.

Brash was able to get an exact fit between some of the dismembered remains and, using anatomical formulae and X-rays, classified other parts as belonging to one body or the other.

After weeks of work, two partially reconstructed bodies lay side by side on tables in the laboratory. 'No 1' was less complete than 'No 2', but Brash had gauged the living stature of the bodies as, respectively, five feet and five feet and three inches.

There was ample evidence that both bodies were female. If — a very large 'if' at this stage — they were of the women from 2 Dalton Square Lancaster, then 'No 1' was Mary Rogerson and 'No 2' was Mrs Ruxton.

With help from an odontologist, Arthur Hutchinson,

15

Brash estimated the age of 'No 1' as twenty (as was the nursemaid) and that of 'No 2' as being between thirty-five and forty-five (Isabella Ruxton was thirty-four).

Paradoxically, many of the mutilations of the remains assisted the pathologists in their search for evidence. The manner of dismemberment (without the use of a saw and with only slight damage to the separated parts), together with the fact that components that might have indicated cause of death had been removed, showed that the criminal was skilled in the use of surgical knives and that he had anatomical and medical knowledge.

The criminal had removed from both heads the eyes, ears, lips and nose — in all of which signs of asphyxia might be found — but so far as body No 2 was concerned, there remained several indications that death was due to asphyxia by throttling.

The most iterated example of 'negative evidence' comes from fiction — the dog that, as Sherlock Holmes noted, did not bark in the night. For a real-life example, it would be hard to better what the experts in the Ruxton investigation noted as being absent from the remains.

Virtually from the start, John Glaister and his colleagues supposed that the reason for many of the mutilations was to make identification more difficult, but it was not until the scientists knew some of the distinguishing features of the two missing women that they began to suspect answers to specific questions.

Perhaps the eyes of body No 1 had been taken out because Mary Rogerson had a cast in one eye. Had the skin been removed from the upper part of the right forearm because Mary had a conspicuous birthmark there? Were the soft tissues shaved from the right thumb because the nursemaid had a scar there?

And had the nose of body No 2 been cut off, and the teeth been extracted, because those were prominent features of Mrs Ruxton? Had the soft tissues of the legs been removed because Isabella's legs were the same thickness from the knees to the ankles? Were the toes lopped off because Isabella's were 'humped'?

So many of the sites of the excisions and mutilations corresponded with those of distinguishing features of the missing women that there seemed only one answer. Added to the evidence already gathered, the 'negative evidence' virtually proved that the bodies were those of Isabella Ruxton and Mary Rogerson.

But to make assurance double sure, James Brash did something that, so far as is known, had never been attempted in a criminal investigation. After obtaining photographs of the missing women, he arranged for the head and shoulders in each to be enlarged to life-size. He took immense care to ensure that the size of the enlargements was correct; for instance, a piece of jewellery worn by Mrs Ruxton in one of the photographs was located and measured to the nearest millimetre, so that the size could be used to establish the measurements of her head and features. The enlarged photographs were then superimposed on photographs, taken to the exact size, of the decapitated heads in the laboratory. The resulting 'double exposures' showed a remarkable correspondence.

On Saturday, 12 October, after the evidence assembled by the Scottish scientists had been added to that gathered by the police, Chief Constable Vann invited Buck Ruxton to his office.

The doctor arrived at 9.30 in the evening and spent the next ten hours answering questions. Then he was charged with the murder of Mary Rogerson.

He looked flabbergasted. 'Most emphatically not,' he spluttered. 'Of course not. The farthest thing from my mind. What motive and why? What are you talking about?'

Following Ruxton's arrest (on 5 November he was further charged with the murder of Isabella), the investigators searched the house in Dalton Square for more indications of his guilt.

They found a good many, of which the most important, perhaps, was a sheet that had precisely the same peculiar fault in the selvedge as did pieces of a sheet that had been used as wrapping for the hideous bundles found at Moffatt.

By the start of the new year, the investigators believed that the case against Buck Ruxton was complete, watertight.

But then they learned something that worried them greatly: the doctor was to be defended at the trial by the velvet-voiced Norman Birkett, who was thought of by some people as 'the courtroom magician', by others as 'the murderer's best friend'.

If anyone could persuade the jury in the Ruxton case to return a nonsensical verdict, it was Birkett.

The trial started on Monday, 2 March 1936, at the old Manchester Assize Court in Great Ducie Street, with Mr Justice Singleton, a stickler for the niceties of courtroom behaviour, presiding.

J. C. Jackson, one of the best-known silks on the Northern circuit, led for the Crown, assisted by two barristers who would rise to high positions in government: one, a Socialist, was Hartley Shawcross, and the other, a Tory, inspired the couplet:

> The closest thing to death in life
> Is David Patrick Maxwell Fyfe.

Buck Ruxton's defender, the tall, bespectacled Norman Birkett, made few notes during the opening speech for the prosecution; but right from the start, Ruxton, sitting in the dock behind Birkett, scribbled messages to his counsel.

According to Mr Jackson's view of what had happened in the house in Dalton Square, Lancaster, after Mrs Ruxton's trip to see the Blackpool illuminations: 'When she went up to bed, a violent quarrel took place; Ruxton strangled his wife, and Mary Rogerson caught him in the act and had to die also.'

There was, of course, much more to Mr Jackson's speech than that; he dealt with every aspect of the case, occasionally in greater detail than some observers thought necessary, starting with the discovery of the human remains at Moffatt and concluding with the arrest of the Indian doctor.

The speech went on till late in the afternoon, leaving only enough time for four prosecution witnesses to be called that day. Though the evidence of those witnesses was formal — to do with plans, photographs and the like — Norman Birkett cross-examined each of them in some depth.

And during the following seven days of the trial, hardly any of the prosecution witnesses — over a hundred of them — left the court without having been questioned by Birkett. At times, when there was a flurry of requests by counsel for the production of exhibits, the well of the court looked like an untidy jumble sale, with bottles, jewellery, books and kitchenware scattered over piles of clothing, carpets and bed-linen.

Mrs Mary Hampshire, one of the several women who had laboured to make the doctor's house presentable after the disappearance of Mrs Ruxton and the nursemaid, fainted in the witness box. Perhaps the sight of some bloodstained carpets, given to her by the generous doctor but taken from her by the police and now exhibits, made her feel queasy. As she was being carried from the court, the doctor peered from the dock at his former patient and gave his professional opinion that she would be all right. When she returned, he made a what-did-I-tell-you? gesture, then started scribbling again.

The last of the Crown's witnesses were the Scottish scientists who had made medico-legal history by their reconstruction and scrutiny of the bodies. They had done their work so thoroughly that Birkett scored few, and then only minor, successes in cross-examination.

Before the last of the scientists was called, Birkett wrote a memorandum for Ruxton's solicitor to show his client. It ended:

'In my clear and very strong view, if Dr Ruxton desires to give evidence, we should confine our evidence to him, and exercise our right of the last word to the jury. . . . Any other course, in my view, would be absolutely fatal.'

Ruxton agreed, and on the morning of the eighth day of the trial was escorted from the dock to be the sole witness in his own defence.

His solicitor had warned him that he must remain calm, listen carefully to each question, and restrict his answers to what had been asked, but the flashily handsome doctor soon forgot — or, believing that he knew best, ignored — the advice.

After asking a few 'tuning-up' questions, Birkett inquired about Ruxton's relations with Isabella — and was made most unhappy by the reply: 'If I may be permitted to put it in appropriate English, I can honestly say we were the kind of people who could not live with each other and could not live without each other.'

Not finished yet, Ruxton said something that his counsel didn't understand.

'You have added something else,' Birkett muttered irritably.

'Forgive me the interruption,' said Ruxton, 'but I just used the French proverb, "Who loves most chastises most." My mentality thinks in French, and I have to translate into English everything you are asking me.'

No doubt feeling that his task was hard enough without the imposition of a language barrier, Birkett from now on tried to leap in with a question as soon as Ruxton had delivered the first sentence of his answer to the previous one.

But Birkett was rarely fast enough, and eventually snapped, 'Perhaps you will just deal only with the questions I put to you.'

No use: the words continued to tumble out, and every so often Ruxton burst into tears.

His answers to two successive questions are often quoted to exemplify how witnesses should not respond.

Birkett asked, 'It is suggested here by the Crown that on the morning of the Sunday after your wife had come back, you killed her?'

'That is an absolute and deliberate and fantastic story,' the doctor screamed, waving his arms about. 'You might just as well say the sun was rising in the west and setting in the east.'

20

Next question: 'It is suggested also by the Crown that, upon that morning, you killed Mary Rogerson?'

'That is absolute bunkum, with a capital B, if I may say it. Why should I kill my poor Mary?'

It may be that the jury never made up their minds about that — or about the motive for Isabella's murder — but after another couple of days, which included the cross-examination of Ruxton, the closing speeches, and the judge's summing-up, the jury returned a verdict of Guilty.

Asked if he had anything to say why sentence of death should not be passed, Ruxton raised his right hand, the palm towards the judge, in what could have been a salute or a blessing, and uttered some flowery but irrelevant remarks. He made the same gesture as the judge spoke the final words of the death sentence, then bowed before being escorted from the dock.

Six weeks later, after the doctor's appeal was dismissed, something rather odd happened. In towns from one end of the country to the other, masses of people, few of them certifiably insane, signed petitions for a reprieve; in Lancaster alone, there were six thousand signatories.

But the Home Secretary had the good sense to ignore the petitions, and Ruxton was hanged at Strangeways Prison, Manchester, on the fine morning of Tuesday, 12 May.

The following Sunday, anyone who had signed a petition and was also a reader of the *News of the World* should have been a trifle embarrassed. There on the front page was a facsimile of a confession to the two murders that the good doctor had written the day after he was arrested.

Postscripts

1. Speaking of the 'Cyclops' eye in one of Ruxton's parcels, R. H. Blundell and G. Haswell Wilson, the editors of *Trial of Buck Ruxton* in the Notable British Trials series (Hodge, Edinburgh; 1936), note a strange, some might think eerie, literary/criminous coincidence: Section II, 'The Vision of Sudden Death', of *The English*

Mail-Coach, written by Thomas de Quincey more than a hundred years before the Ruxton Case, contains this passage: 'But what was Cyclops doing here? Had the medical men recommended northern air, or how? I collected, from such explanations as he volunteered, that he had an interest at stake in some suit-in-law now pending at Lancaster.'

2. The American crime historian, Jeffrey Bloomfield, has suggested to me that there may be a more salient instance of nature imitating art in the Ruxton case:

My idea goes like this:

(*a*) As part of his quaint notion of an alibi for the night of the murders, Ruxton claimed that, several nights later, he went to see the Ronald Colman film *Clive of India* at the County Cinema, next door to 2 Dalton Square.

(*b*) The fact that he was of Indian background made him particularly aware of that title, but for our purposes he was aware of current movies.

(*c*) In 1932, Dashiell Hammett wrote the crime novel, *The Thin Man*. In it, the killer murders the title-character, digs a hole in the floor of his victim's laboratory, and after partially destroying the body with lime (shades of the Manning murder case), plants various items, such as a long belt and trousers, near the body to make the remains look like those of a fat person, not a 'thin man'.

(*d*) The movie version of the book, starring William Powell and Myrna Loy as the detective Nick Charles and his wife Nora, was released in 1934. (It received its London première in the June. As the County Cinema did not advertise in the *Lancaster Guardian*, there seems no way of finding out whether or not it was shown there.) The script-writers made slight adjustments to the business of the discovery of the skeleton and the clothes.

(*e*) We cannot be sure what gave Ruxton his plan, for his killing of his wife was almost certainly an act of sudden fury, and he probably killed Mary

Rogerson so as to silence her as a witness. However, I think the movie may have given Ruxton the idea of how to get rid of, and to disguise, the victim's remains. The curious thing is that he never noticed that in both the novel and the film the murderer is caught (and presumably convicted). In fact, in the novel, Nick says this to Nora when she asks if the murderer has confessed: 'Why should he? You can't plead guilty of murder in the first degree. There were too many murders – and at least two of them were too obviously done in cold blood – for the District Attorney to let him plead guilty of second-degree murder. There's nothing for him to do but fight it out.'

Ruxton may have subconsciously skimmed that part, if he read the novel. It is not in the movie version, and if he got his idea from the movie it really was too bad for him. As I said before, the first murder was almost certainly one of passion, and I have sometimes felt that if a few minutes had elapsed before the nursemaid appeared, Ruxton might have regained his composure and reacted differently. He panicked when he saw that the nursemaid was a witness, and killed her (keep in mind that he was still in a fury from the anger towards his wife). It doesn't excuse the double murder, but I have an idea that if he had had a 'breather', he would have calmed down and carefully considered his position. Whether he would have proceeded with trying to hide his crime, I cannot say, but it is possible that he would have surrendered himself to the police. He might have gotten away with manslaughter for the killing of his wife. But that is just my opinion. . . .

3. From the *Manchester Evening News*, 14 January 1983:

The bath-tub in which Dr Buck Ruxton chopped up his common-law wife and his nursemaid still survives – as a drinking trough for police horses. . . .

Few know that the white enamel tub – Exhibit 'A' at the sensational trial at the Manchester Assize Court – is now at the police stables at Longton, near Preston.

23

The tub spent many years in the 'black museum' of the forensic laboratories at Lancashire Constabulary headquarters at Preston before being moved to Longton. It carries a brass plaque:

'This bath was used by Dr Buck Ruxton when mutilating the bodies of his wife and his maid on an unknown date between the 14th and the 29th September, 1935, at 2 Dalton Square, Lancaster.'

4. In 1985, Henry Vann, the former Chief Constable of Lancaster, was interviewed by Roger Wilkes for a BBC Radio Four programme on the case in a series entitled *An Infamous Address*. He said, among other things:

When Ruxton was about to be hanged, I was pleasantly surprised to receive a letter from him, from the prison:

My dear Vann,

May I make a dying request? Oh please do be good to my children. Mr Gardner, my solicitor, is their trustee. You will not fail me, will you? Those children have never known a mother's love, and they have lost a father's care.... In your lifetime please make a practice of enquiring after my children and seeing to their welfare at least once every six months. It is not asking too much, is it?

Promise me, a dying man, you will be good enough to take an interest in the wellbeing of my three children. Be a friend to them, dear Vann, I implore you, I beseech thee. I will bless you and yours from above if simply you be good to my children.

I don't bear the slightest spite against you. Shake hands. Remember me to all....

Yours,

BUCK RUXTON

I fulfilled my promise to look after the children, which I did with regularity over many years. They all made good.

The Wives of Dr Bowers

EDWARD H. SMITH

BETWEEN THE YEARS 1885 and 1888, there played in San Francisco one of the strangest and most tangled dramas of the poison flask ever witnessed in this or any other land. I refer to the several trials growing out of the death of the wife of Dr J. Milton Bowers in November of the former year.

Dr Bowers, born in Baltimore in 1843, studied in his native land until he was twenty. Then he went to Berlin and dabbled about the university there for a time, not as a regularly enrolled student, but as an irregular attendant of lectures and a witness of surgical operations. Towards the end of 1863, he returned home, joined the Union Army, and served without special distinction until the end of the Civil War.

With the cessation of conflict came the beginning of Dr Bowers' matrimonial career — one that saw many changes of scene and of mates. The first wife, who had been Miss Fannie Hammet, he married in Chicago in 1865. In 1873 Mrs Bowers died. Her husband had attended her in her final illness and certified the cause of her death. No rumours or doubts arose at the time, but afterwards it was asserted that the first Mrs Bowers' death had been attended by 'suspicious circumstances'.

Shortly after the demise of his first wife, Dr Bowers went to Brooklyn and established himself there as a practitioner. He prospered in a small way and soon met Miss Theresa Shirk, a beautiful and talented young actress of German extraction. They were married after a short courtship and left a little later for San Francisco, whither they were drawn by two considerations — the impaired health of the wife and the possibility of better opportunities for the doctor.

Dr and Mrs Bowers dwelt in seeming amity for seven years, but, on 29 January 1881, the comely wife died suddenly at the Palace Hotel. Here, again, there were no proceedings against Dr Bowers nor yet any appearances sufficiently suggestive to call public attention to the man. The circumstances under which the second wife died did not, in fact, come to be questioned and investigated until some years later, when an event of more sinister proportions brought the whole past of the physician under scrutiny.

Dr Bowers' second wife was still alive when he met and began to woo another woman, Mrs Cecilia Benhayon Levy, who had just previously been divorced from Sylvian Levy. She had a little daughter by her first husband.

The relatives of Mrs Levy were no wise willing to have her married to Dr Bowers, partly because of religious difference, partly because of fancied social distinctions, and partly because there was some little question about the end of the second Mrs Bowers. She, however, despite their protests took her place in Dr Bowers' household as the third wife. The ceremony was performed on 19 July 1881, less than six months after the death of the second spouse.

The bearing of this history of marriages and deaths and remarriages on the poison case will become apparent presently.

The tenure of bliss with the third mate was much more brief than in the earlier instances. In the summer of 1885 Mrs Bowers was taken very ill. Her husband treated her, but not to the satisfaction of her relatives, who summoned first Dr W. H. Bruner of San Francisco and, a month later, Dr Martin of Oakland. The young woman's body was swollen in an extraordinary way. Her whole physical and facial aspect was changed — yet she displayed, even in the midst of her sufferings, a remarkably clear and beautiful complexion, such as is sometimes induced by the arsenic treatment. Her sufferings were most acute in the progress of frequent convulsions.

The relatives of the suffering woman, especially her mother, who had become reconciled to her daughter when she was told of her peril, seem to have been suspicious of Dr Bowers from the first, perhaps only because they had always disliked him. Mrs Benhayon – the mother – offered more substantial grounds for her fears, however. She knew that Bowers had caused his wife to take out various insurances on her life, which aggregated seventeen thousand dollars. She had demanded that Mrs Bowers' daughter, Tillie, the child of her first union, be made the beneficiary of some of this insurance, and when this was not done, she regarded the doctor with all the more misgiving.

The suspicion under which Dr Bowers laboured in the course of his wife's illness finally expressed itself in two mysterious happenings. On the afternoon of 28 October, a stranger entered the San Francisco office of the American Legion of Honour, a fraternal order in which Mrs Bowers held a five-thousand-dollar policy, and asked whether he might inspect the roster of members of the order in San Francisco. He was informed that this was not permitted, whereupon he told Secretary Burton that a woman member of the order was very ill and would die in a few days – as the result of 'foul play'. He would not say who he was, and hurried away, leaving only a vague impression in Mr Burton's mind.

Five days later, on 2 November, a mysterious man, possibly the same person, hurried into the coroner's office and told an attendant that Mrs Bowers had just died, that there were suspicious circumstances, and that an investigation should be made forthwith. While the official who received this information turned his back to make a note, the man slipped out of the door and vanished. No trace of him could be discovered and he was never identified.

The coroner, Dr C. C. O'Donnell, less bound by formality than a more modern official might be, decided to waste no time, and appeared soon afterwards at the Bowers' home, in the Arcade House, at 930 Market Street. He found the woman dead in bed and her husband near by, evidently preparing her body for the coming of the undertaker. Dr Bowers expressed no surprise at the unheralded visit of the coroner and conducted himself with the utmost coolness and confidence. His wife had been ill for more than four months, and under the care of at least two reputable physicians other than himself. She had died of a cancer or abscess of the liver; in this diagnosis the other physicians had concurred with him. The coroner might perform an autopsy and make any examinations he thought proper, but he had better make them at once, as it was intended to bury the body on the following day.

The coroner was, however, not beguiled by this display of sang-froid. He summoned a board of six physicians and surgeons, opened the body, found that there was no diseased condition of the liver, and came upon evidences of phosphorus poisoning. The stomach and other organs were removed and sent to Dr W. D. Johnson, Professor of Chemistry at Cooper Medical College, who shortly reported the finding of traces of the poison. The coroner's jury returned a verdict on 12 November, charging Bowers with having caused the death of his wife by administrations of phosphorus, and he was promptly clapped into jail.

Even before the formal charge and arrest of Bowers, an interesting state of affairs had revealed itself at the Bowers' home. While the doctor's mother-in-law and the other relatives of his wife were solidly against him and most vehement in their expressions of belief in his guilt, it was found that Mrs Zeissing, the dead woman's nurse, and Miss Theresa Farrell, the Bowers' housekeeper, were quite as determinedly on the other side of the fence, trying in every way to shield and justify the doctor and to divert suspicion from him. They went so far on his behalf that actual suspicion attached to them in connection with the source of the poison.

It was believed that Dr Bowers had got his phosphorus from samples of various medicines which had been sent to him by manufacturers and druggists. The investigators came to this conclusion when they found that Bowers had not bought phosphorus anywhere. The doctor rather defiantly admitted that he had received samples of the kind indicated; but when the police arrived to search his office, everything of the kind had been cleverly and carefully done away with so that no trace remained and no evidence of possession could ever be obtained. The theory that the nurse and housekeeper had disposed of these matters for their employer was advanced and broadly accepted.

Bowers was not brought to trial until the following spring. On 8 March 1886, he was called before Judge Murphy in the superior court, and the case was under examination. The prosecution was managed by the noted West Coast attorney, Eugene Duprey.

Duprey told the jury that Bowers had killed his wife for a double motive — getting possession of her insurance money and putting her out of the way so that he might marry a younger woman from San José, whom he was already courting. He said that it would be shown that Bowers had courted the dead woman before his earlier — his second — wife had died. He also announced that an attempt would be made to show that both the first and second wives had died under the most suggestive circumstances. Furthermore, he charged that Mrs Zeissing and Miss Farrell were in league with the doctor.

The trial itself was not of special interest. It revolved, in the main, about expert medical testimony, for and against the accused man. The State, as in so many other poison cases, set up the theory that the indications found at the post-mortem examination could have been caused by nothing other than the specific poison named, and that the finding of traces of such poison in the organs of the victim clinched the case. Bowers, like so many before him and after him, tried to show, by contrary expert testimony, that similar indications might result from ordinary disease and that the amount of phosphorus present was not enough to account for the death.

After more than six weeks, the case went to the jury on the afternoon of 23 April, and the same night a verdict of guilty was returned. Bowers was sentenced to be hanged on 2 June, but an appeal to the State supreme court was immediately taken and the doctor was locked into the county jail to await the outcome of this move. In those days the California courts moved with a deliberation that overshadowed even the leisureliness of Eastern justice. So it happened that Dr Bowers was still in jail waiting for the result of his appeal on Sunday, 23 October 1887 – exactly eighteen months after his conviction – when a stranger series of events happened.

About noon of the day in question, a Mrs Higgson, who conducted a rooming house at No 22 Geary Street, sent word to the coroner that a man had died in one of her rooms. The coroner was dumbfounded to discover that the dead man was the brother of Cecilia Benhayon Bowers, but his astonishment was as nothing to the consternation that seized him when he began to search the room and ask questions.

Mrs Higgson informed the coroner that she had never seen the dead man, Henry Benhayon, before, and that she had not rented him the room, but had let it to another man several days before. The circumstances under which the room had been rented were peculiar. On the 18th, according to the landlady, a young man had called and asked to rent the room, whose number was 21. It was occupied at the time and she tried to rent her caller another room, but he said he was interested only in No 21, and went away. The following day, another man came and asked about the room. He, too, was told that the room was occupied, but on further inquiry was told that it would be vacant on Saturday the 22nd, which was three days removed. He paid a deposit of five dollars and was given a key, with the understanding that his tenancy was to begin on Saturday. Mrs Higgson saw no more of this man or of anyone else connected with the affair until Sunday, when she entered room 21 with a pass-key, prompted both by curiosity and by the need of cleaning the room. Benhayon, the dead man, was not the man who had inquired after the room on the 18th nor yet the man who had rented it on the 19th.

In the room, near the body, which was laid out on top of the bedclothes, as if prepared by an undertaker, were three bottles, all closely corked. One contained whisky, one chloroform liniment, and one cyanide of potassium. From the last the label had been removed and part of the original contents was missing.

There were also three letters in the room, which are of importance to the consideration of this most mysterious affair. They follow:

21 October, 1887.

To the Editor of the *Chronicle*.

Sir,
Inclosed find one dollar to pay for this advertisement and the balance for a reward. I will call in a few days.

Yours truly,   HENRY BENHAYON

This advertisement was enclosed:

Lost, on October 20th, near the City Hall, a memorandum book with a letter. A liberal reward will be paid if left at this office.

The second letter read:

City, 22 October, 1887.

Dr J. Milton Bowers,
I only ask that you do not molest my mother. Tillie is not responsible for my acts and I have made all reparation in my power.

I likewise caution you against some of your friends who knew Cecilia only as a husband should.

Among them are C. M. McLennan and others whose names I cannot think of now, but you will find some more when the memorandum book is found. Farewell.

Yours,   H. BENHAYON.

The last communication was intended and headed as a 'confession'. It read:

> The history of the tragedy commenced after my sister married Dr Bowers.
>
> I had reasons to believe that he would leave her soon, as they always quarrelled and on one occasion she told me that she would poison him before she would permit him to leave her.
>
> I said in jest, 'Have him insured.'
>
> She said 'All right,' but Bowers objected for a long time, but finally said: 'If it will keep you out of mischief, go ahead.'
>
> They both joined several lodges and I got the stuff ready to dispose of him, but my sister would not listen to the proposition and threatened to expose me.
>
> After my sister got sick I felt an irresistible impulse to use the stuff on her and finish him afterwards. I would then become administrator for my little niece, Tillie, and would have the benefit of the insurance.
>
> I think it was on Friday, 24 November, 1885, that I took one capsule out of her pill box and filled it with two kinds of poison. [He probably intended to write 24 October.] I didn't think Bowers could get into any trouble, as the person who gave me the poison told me it would leave no trace in the stomach. This person committed suicide before the trial, and as it might implicate others if I mention his name I will close the tragedy.
>
> H. BENHAYON.
>
> P.S. I took Dr Bowers' money out of his desk when my sister died.

An autopsy was immediately performed and it was found that Benhayon had died as the result of a dose of cyanide of potassium. At the same time, handwriting experts were called to compare the letters with writings definitely done by the dead man. The results were not very satisfactory, for some of the experts decided that the letters were genuine, while others held that they were forgeries.

There arose the natural and inevitable question, full of

the darkest implications: Had Benhayon actually killed his sister and then committed suicide, when he saw that Bowers was likely to hang; or had someone else killed Benhayon and prepared these strange notes in an effort to clear and save Bowers?

The State of California immediately took the latter position and sought feverishly for the offender. Since Bowers himself had been securely locked in jail for eighteen months and more, he could not have done the deed, but those in communication with him were at once suspected, and the detectives carried a firm line of suspicion to the person of a young man named John Dimmig, who had married Bowers' housekeeper, Theresa Farrell. The reader will remember that Miss Farrell and Mrs Zeissing, the nurse, had been suspected of unwarranted prejudice in favour of Dr Bowers and accused by the prosecutor at the Bowers trial of collusion with the doctor in the murder of his wife.

It was accordingly believed that Dimmig had killed Benhayon and prepared the notes at the suggestion of his wife, who frequently visited the captive doctor in jail, accompanied by Mrs Zeissing. Just why these two should have wanted to aid further the convicted physician at such great peril to themselves is not clear, though it was suggested they might have been forced to act for Bowers by his threat of exposing their complicity in his deed.

The first bit of evidence against Dimmig was obtained when he was shown to Mrs Higgson, the keeper of the rooming house, and identified as the man who had tried to rent room No 21 on the 18th. He then admitted that he had made an inquiry about the room but said it was a 'stall'. He had really visited the house as a book agent, and had asked about rooms in order to get inside. Later he changed his story and said he had wanted the room because he had an appointment with a woman from San José, who had written him and told him to engage a room for Saturday night. He said he did not know the address of this woman, and knew her only by the name of Timkins. He denied having sent anyone else to rent the room for him and protested that he had been drunk on the 19th, the day the room was let to the second man for occupancy on Saturday. He had accidentally met Benhayon on that day, and had possibly told him something about the room in the course of his intoxicated wanderings. He said he had not met the Timkins woman as was planned, had not seen Benhayon again, and had not been near the room. But he finally turned over to the police the following letter:

City, 22 October, 1887.

J. A. DIMMIG.

Sir: Call on me at once. I am in a devilish fix. I don't want your money, but your advice. I think it is all up with me. You will find me in room 21, No 22 Geary Street.

HENRY BENHAYON.

This letter was in the same handwriting as that which produced the letters above cited, and once again the graphologists disagreed as to its genuineness as the writing of Benhayon.

The letter had been addressed to Dimmig at the office of the Western Perfumery Co, where he occasionally did some business but where he did not often receive mail. Strangely enough, soon after the letter reached the company, Dimmig called and asked if there was any mail for him. The letter was then handed over — but, in spite of its character and of the strange coincidence that Benhayon was 'in a devilish fix' in the very room which Dimmig had tried to rent four days earlier, Dimmig told the police that he paid no attention to the communication. He said he had not gone near Benhayon or the Geary Street address.

Dimmig also told the police and the prosecutor that he had never possessed any cyanide of potassium, but it was discovered by the detectives that he had tried to buy this poison in several drug stores and had finally procured it from an apothecary named Lacey.

The police found that Benhayon, far from having

expressed any sympathy for Bowers, had shown the deepest hatred of the doctor, and told all who knew him that he was absolutely confident of his guilt. Benhayon was last seen alive on the night preceding the finding of his body, at about eleven o'clock. He was then noticeably drunk or drugged and was in the company of a man and a woman who could never be found and identified.

The officers also found that Dimmig had, on Friday evening, gone to a book store in Bush Street and there bought some books for Mrs Zeissing, his wife's co-worker in the Bowers' home. At that time Dimmig had displayed a bottle of whisky similar to the one found at the deathbed of Benhayon.

As the result of all these discoveries, Dimmig was formally charged with the murder of Benhayon, by Captain Lees of the detective force, on 12 November 1887, exactly two years after Bowers had been likewise formally charged with the murder of his wife, Benhayon's sister.

Dimmig was placed on trial on 10 February 1888, before the same Judge Murphy who had conducted the trial of Bowers. The case went to the jury on 14 March and resulted in a disagreement after more than sixteen hours of wrangling and squabbling. In December of the same year, the second trial was called, also before Judge Murphy, and this time the expected happened. Juries called to consider murder cases in which there has previously been a disagreement very rarely bring in a verdict against the accused. They probably proceed on the theory of refusing to accept a responsibility which a first panel of jurors declined. So, at Dimmig's second exposure to the jeopardy of death, his peers, after twenty-three hours of disputation, agreed to set him free.

While all this had been going on, Bowers was still in jail. He was waiting for the decision of the supreme court when Benhayon was found dead and his dramatic confession was published and discussed. A short time afterwards, a higher tribunal handed down a decision in which a new trial was ordered on account of slight errors in the conduct of the case and the inconclusiveness of some of the testimony. Now that Dimmig had been acquitted of the murder of Benhayon, the natural if not legal inference to be drawn was that the confession of Benhayon would have to be accepted as authentic. The actual state of affairs was this:

The brother of the dead woman had been found dead with a confession beside him, which accused himself and cleared Bowers. This confession was regarded as genuine by some experts and as a forgery by others. The State had decided that it was a forgery and attempted to prove that Dimmig had concocted and carried out a scheme to save Bowers, of which scheme the murder of Benhayon and the forgery of the confession were parts. But a jury had now acquitted Dimmig of the murder. That being so, it was probable that he could not be convicted as a forger and that the confession could not be excluded from a retrial of Bowers. That worthy would certainly insist on showing that another man had confessed the crime for which he was being tried.

The San Francisco district attorney, in spite of loud protests from a part of the public and the newspapers, could do nothing but dismiss the Bowers case and save the community the expense of a futile trial. So Bowers walked out a free man and the central figure in a case which, so far as I can discover, finds its parallels only in fiction.

Immediately after his release from jail, he married a young woman from San José, a Miss Bird, if memory does not trick me. With her he lived happily and obscurely enough until his death in 1905.

Poison of One Kind or Another

HAROLD EATON

SINCE THE DAYS of the Borgias, poison has always been the weapon of the gentleman murderer. The more subtle the drug, the more secret the administration of it, the greater the artistic triumph. Knowledge of the properties of the various poisons postulates a certain mental ability, and rarely does one find a man of education guilty of so vulgar a gesture as a knife-thrust or a blow with a poker. Palmer was a man of some social position; Pritchard and Lamson, the subject of this sketch, both had medical qualifications and possessed a considerable degree of culture; while even Seddon achieves a certain gentility through the method he employed to gain his ends.

Dr George Henry Lamson seems to have been born with a genius for friendship, and to have acquired a reputation for humanity. In 1876 and 1877 he served as a volunteer army-surgeon in Serbia and Romania, and in recognition of his work numerous decorations of both countries were conferred upon him. Not only in England, but in America and on the Continent, he possessed a wide circle of friends, whose efforts to save him after conviction testified to the sincerity of their affection. He was a French scholar, could speak other European tongues, and had read much in many languages; in effect, a young man of experience and promise, a young man whose generous impulses sometimes led him into extravagances, but all the same a young man who would sober down one of these days and make his mark in the world. That his name will live for some while yet in the memory of man seems to be assured. . . .

In 1876, when he was in his twenty-sixth year, this young man of promise married. His wife, a Miss John, was a ward in chancery, and upon marriage became entitled to a small fortune which, since the Married Women's Property Act was not then law, passed under the control of her husband. Among the new relations that this alliance brought to Lamson must be noticed Herbert John and Percy John, his wife's brothers, and Mrs Chapman, her sister.

In 1879 Herbert John died suddenly under circumstances which, though they aroused no suspicion at the time, seem to indicate that the crime for which Lamson was executed was not his first murder. At all events, through the death of her brother Mrs Lamson became entitled to some £700, and with this money her husband purchased a medical practice at Bournemouth. As a doctor, Lamson was unsuccessful, and his circumstances went from bad to worse, until finally the home was sold up. In April of 1881 he went to America; but whatever venture he attempted out there met with no better fortune than had his practice at Bournemouth, and he actually arrived back in England with nothing save £5 borrowed from the surgeon on board. That he was in desperate need of money there can be no doubt. A few pounds might still be borrowed; were, in fact, borrowed from friends — but friends, though willing to help, were not rich. A large sum, a thousand pounds or more, was needed to square Lamson's debts and to set him upon his feet again.

It is possible to trace the mental processes that induced this young man, with a reputation for humanity and a genius for friendship, to turn, in his search for money, first to fraud and forgery and finally to the gravest crime known to the law. Some years earlier he had become addicted to the morphine habit, contracted while serving in the Balkans, and he himself attributed his downfall to this cause. Probably his failure as a doctor was due to the drug, which disinclines the mind for a punctual routine of work; probably also his ethical perception was blurred by the use of the needle. It is charitable to suppose that the latter proposition at all events is true, for it may serve to palliate in some small measure what was possibly the most cunning and diabolical crime of the nineteenth century.

Without any very extravagant tastes, Lamson was yet not accustomed to stinting himself, and his generosity urged him to treat his friends more lavishly than his means warranted. He now had to provide for a wife and child, but his addiction to the morphine habit prevented him from pursuing any ordered and regular business. That had been tried and had failed. Experience and skill in his profession he certainly had, but he was unable to subdue the lethargy from which all drug-takers suffer. What, then, was to be done? Debtors were pressing and friends were not so staunch and cordial as they had been — were, in fact, disinclined to lend money without any security whatsoever.

Other means must be found. He had still a banking account — overdrawn, it must be admitted — but he could write cheques which by some remote chance might be honoured. Moreover, his medical qualifications inspired tradesmen with a certain amount of confidence and induced them to grant credit up to a point. Small sums could be obtained in this way — not quite honestly, perhaps, but one never knew whether a bank was bluffing or not when it declared that no further cheques would be met.

These minor successes were all very well, but they were only temporary measures. In the end he grew more reckless, and, as will be shown later, drew and cashed a cheque for £12 10s. upon a bank at which he had never had an account, though it is probable that at that time he had resolved upon murder, and was trying to provide himself with the money necessary to leave England. If he was still debating the issue, the difficulty which had attended this fraud and the paltry proceeds of it determined him. He had committed an offence for which he might receive a severe sentence, and what had he gained by it? A dozen pounds. These petty dishonesties were not worthwhile, were unworthy of his talents. What was needed was a big coup.

This excursion into crime was dangerous and amateurish enough: fraud, it would seem, was not his *métier*. Yet money had to be obtained from somewhere. He hadn't had much luck in the course of his life; just one slice and one slice only — the legacy from Herbert John.

The day before his execution, Lamson, while confessing that he had been rightly convicted, vehemently denied that he had been in any way concerned in the death of Herbert John. If for the moment we accept this statement, the fatal illness of his brother-in-law must have appeared to Lamson as an extremely opportune accident — an accident which, unfortunately, could not be repeated. Was there no one else by whose death he might hope to profit?

The answer was not far to seek. Were the other brother-in-law, Percy Malcolm John, to die unmarried and before attaining the age of twenty-one, half of the £3000 which he would inherit upon either of these contingencies would pass to Mrs Lamson. At the time of his death in 1881, Percy John was eighteen and was living at Blenheim House School, Wimbledon. A cripple from birth, he suffered from curvature of the spine and his lower limbs were paralysed. He had therefore to propel himself about in a wheel-chair and to rely upon his schoolfellows to carry him up and down stairs. Apart from his disability, he seems to have enjoyed good health and to have possessed a cheerful disposition, which secured him many friends. His holidays he frequently passed with Dr Lamson and his sister, to whom he was devotedly attached. That he would live long was improbable, for the curvature was growing worse, but it was equally improbable that he would die in time to save Lamson from bankruptcy, perhaps from prison. One can imagine that the doctor watched impatiently the slow progress of the disease, until at last his desperate need of money tempted him to assist nature. The boy could only live a few more years at most, could find but little in life to enjoy. Would not death be a merciful release?

Whether so humane a sophistry entered his mind, or whether the use of morphia had indeed distorted his sense of proportion to the point of madness, is a problem in psychology that can find no answer. Having made up his mind, he certainly set about his task with the proverbial cunning of the maniac. With the resources of science at his command, he was able to choose a rare and subtle poison which, had he used it more moderately, might have escaped detection and defied any chemical tests known to the analysts of those days.

The weapon which he selected was aconitine, which is the active principle of the plant called 'monks-hood' or 'wolf's-bane', and among the whole range of poisons he could have found nothing more deadly nor more horrible. There is no other recorded case of a murderer employing this drug by itself, and it is as the pioneer of a novel poison that Lamson's name will be remembered.

After his return from America in the summer of 1881, Lamson went to the Isle of Wight, and it was there that he made his first attempt upon the life of Percy John. The boy had come to spend his holidays with his sister at Shanklin, and there is little doubt that during his visit his brother-in-law administered a dose of aconitine to him under the guise of a quinine pill. Whether this was by way of experiment or whether Lamson thought that nature required only a little assistance, is uncertain. At all events, the boy completely recovered, and Lamson, grateful, perhaps, that he had failed, and hoping for some other means of rescue, made no further attempt until the following December. A second trip to America intervened, but it was as unsuccessful as the previous one, and he returned absolutely penniless, even being forced to pawn his watch and chain and a case of surgical instruments for £5.

If after his initial failure he had abandoned his design against his brother-in-law, the urgency of procuring money without delay reinstated the thought in his mind. Money he must have at all costs and, save for fraud and burglary, arts in which he had never graduated, there was no other way. In November 1881, he was staying at Nelson's Hotel, Great Portland Street, and on the 20th he tried to purchase aconitine from Messrs Bell & Co in Oxford Street, but they refused to supply him on the ground that he was unknown to them. Nevertheless, on the 24th he managed to buy two grains of the poison from Messrs Allen & Hanbury, and the ease with which he procured it was made the subject of a comment by the judge and of a recommendation by the jury. All he did — all, in fact, he was required to do by the Poisons Act — was to give his name and address, and without verifying his assertion that he was a doctor, the assistant handed over to him poison sufficient to kill thirty people.

Having made his preparations, Lamson tried to obtain funds to keep him going until he could put his plan into execution. On 26 November he went to the American Exchange office and asked them to cash a cheque on the Wiltshire & Dorset Bank for £15. This the exchange refused to do. Three days later, Lamson, though lacking the money for the fare, managed to get to Ventnor by assuring the railway authorities that his friends there would reimburse them. His idea in going to the Isle of Wight was, no doubt, to try to raise money in a place where he and his family were known, but where the news of his acute poverty had not so far penetrated. In this he was partially successful, for he induced a Mr Price Owen to advance him £20 upon a cheque drawn on the Wiltshire & Dorset Bank. Once the money was in his possession and his fare to London assured, Lamson realised that what he had done amounted probably to the offence of obtaining money by false pretences. He knew well enough that the cheque was worthless and that Mr Owen would discover that fact in a day or two. Time must be gained somehow.

Accordingly he wired to his victim: 'Just discovered that cheque you asked yesterday made on wrong bank. Please don't send it on. Letter follows.' The letter, written from his hotel in London, explained the mistake plausibly and circumstantially. He had formerly had an account at the Wiltshire & Dorset Bank, but had transferred his business elsewhere. Still retaining a few blank cheques upon the former bank, he had stupidly mixed up his old cheque book with his new one. He had wired for the right cheque book and would put the matter straight as soon as it arrived.

Lamson must long before have decided that the murder of Percy John was the only solution of his difficulties; but the safest and swiftest method of administering poison remained to be considered. In a few weeks the boy would be coming to spend his Christmas holidays with him. Should he do it then? He could announce that his brother-in-law, never very strong, was ill; he would, of course, be the boy's medical attendant – could, if necessary, counterfeit symptoms and even sign the certificate of death. Small risk of detection here! And yet, the delay – three weeks! How was he to support himself for those three weeks: how to adjust those little money matters which smelt so strongly of fraud? In any event, it would be a month or two before he would actually receive his wife's share of the boy's estate, but it would be easy to borrow upon his expectations as soon as his brother-in-law was dead. There must be no more hesitation, no more half-hearted, bungling mistakes such as that first attempt of his at Shanklin in the summer. The deed must be done surely and immediately.

Yet this man who had chosen the most subtle of poisons and who had so long pondered over his plans, committed the actual crime so clumsily that he at once fastened suspicion on himself. Perhaps his eagerness betrayed him, perhaps his addiction to morphine prevented him from paying proper attention to detail. He had been a failure in fraud, and now, with every chance of an artistic triumph, he was to become a slipshod murderer.

Having decided to act without delay, he had next to consider what was the best method of administering the poison – a problem that presented few difficulties to one skilled in medicine and possessing the complete confidence of his victim. One other matter still remained to be settled, and that was his conduct after the commission of the crime. Should he return to London and await quietly the painful news of his brother-in-law's sudden death? His nerves were strong, but were they strong enough for that? Was he a good enough actor to sympathise convincingly with his wife's grief and to conceal all signs of satisfaction and eagerness? It would perhaps be safer to leave England for a short time, in case anything untoward occurred, and to claim the £1500 upon his return.

On 1 December he visited a medical student called John Tulloch, a great friend of his, and announced that he would shortly be going to Paris. That he published this news to anyone else, except Mr William Bedbrook, the schoolmaster, seems uncertain, but no doubt he wished to convey a general impression that he had long ago decided to visit Paris, and he cunningly made this trip of his the excuse for going to see Percy John. So affectionate a brother-in-law would naturally wish to say good-bye to the boy – even though he might only be absent a few weeks.

'My dear Percy,' he wrote, 'I had intended running down to Wimbledon to see you today, but I have been delayed by various matters until it is now nearly six o'clock, and by the time I should reach Blenheim House you would probably be preparing for bed. I leave for Paris and Florence to-morrow and wish to see you before going, so I purpose to run down to your place as early as I can for a few minutes, even if I can accomplish no more. Believe me, my dear boy, your loving brother, George Lamson.'

This was written on 1 December, and had he succeeded in putting his schemes into execution the next evening, he would doubtless have left for Paris as stated in the letter. His subsequent excuse – that Mr Bedbrook had told him that there was a bad boat running that night and that he had therefore modified his original plans – was utterly false and became not the weakest link in the chain of suspicion that ultimately led to his arrest. On 2 December he went down to Wimbledon with Tulloch, and, leaving his friend at a public house, went off, ostensibly to call at the school. That he never visited Blenheim House that evening is one of the curious features of the case, and the reason for this manoeuvre seems obscure. It may be that his heart failed him, or it may be that he had forgotten some essential part of his role of poisoner. At all events, he rejoined Tulloch after an absence of twenty minutes and told him that he had seen his brother-in-law and that the poor boy was manifestly weaker. His mournful prophecy that Percy John would not last much longer cannot, perhaps, be cited as an authentic example of clairvoyance.

Probably lack of funds made him withhold his hand upon that day. He had committed himself to a trip abroad, but it is doubtful whether he had sufficient money for the fare. If possible, he must raise the wind just once more in order to induce that long-desired windfall.

He returned to town with Tulloch, and the pair went to the Comedy Theatre in Panton Street. Subsequently Lamson drew a cheque in favour of his friend, whom he asked to cash it for him. As this cheque was upon a bank at which the doctor had not then and never had had an account, this action constituted a grave criminal offence. No doubt he anticipated that the cheque would be returned marked 'No account', and that by then he would have borrowed from some other source sufficient to satisfy Tulloch. The idea of an immediate loan as soon as Percy John was dead must have been one of the chief factors in his schemes, for Tulloch, in spite of their friendship, and in spite of the fact that he and Lamson were rarely out of each other's debt, does not appear to have been the sort of man who would have tried to hush up this transaction.

Ultimately, after a rebuff at the Adelphi Hotel, they succeeded in cashing the cheque at the Eyre Arms, St John's Wood, and Lamson, with the means of escape in his pocket, had now no reason to hesitate or to delay.

The following evening, Tuesday 6 December, a few minutes before seven o'clock, he called at Blenheim House and asked to see Percy John. The latter was carried upstairs to the dining-room, where he found Lamson and Mr Bedbrook, the headmaster, and the three of them sat there chatting for some minutes. That the mental strain of the last few months had told upon the doctor can be deduced from the fact that Mr Bedbrook hardly recognised him upon arrival, and that in answer to the doctor's greeting: 'How fat you are looking, Percy, old boy,' the latter replied: 'I wish I could say the same of you, George.'

Mr Bedbrook then invited his guest to take a glass of sherry, and this the latter accepted, but asked for some white sugar in order to neutralise the alcohol in the wine. The significance of this action is obscure, and though the point was laboured by the prosecution it is doubtful whether this sugar played more than a subsidiary part in Lamson's scheme. The doctor had with him a bag, and from this he took a Dundee cake and some sweets. It has been suggested that the cake was already cut, and, according to many accounts, Mr Bedbrook expressly stated this fact in his evidence; but the shorthand note of the trial is silent upon the point, and the theory must therefore be accepted with a certain amount of caution.

Lamson handed a piece of the cake to Percy John and to Mr Bedbrook, and took a slice himself; all three of them ate some of the sweets. After some further conversation, Lamson turned to Mr Bedbrook and remarked apropos of nothing: 'While in America I did not forget you. I have bought these capsules for you. You will find them very useful to give the boys medicine. I should like you to try one and see how easily they can be swallowed.' As he spoke, he produced a half-empty box of capsules from his bag, gave one of them to Mr Bedbrook and then, shovelling some of the sugar into another one, said: 'Here, Percy, you are a swell pill-taker: take this and show Mr Bedbrook how easily it can be swallowed.' The boy complied, and Lamson at once said: 'I must be going now.'

Though Blenheim House was less than a minute's walk from the station, the next train left at 7.21, and it was then already 7.20. Mr Bedbrook pointed this out to Lamson and suggested that he should go by the next train, the 7.50; but the other refused, declaring that he would miss the boat-train from Victoria unless he went at once. However, he stayed a minute or more saying good-bye, and it was past 7.21 when he left the school. It may also be noted that he succeeded in catching the boat train, and crossed to France that night. Not knowing how soon the poison would work, and distrusting his powers of dissimulation, he determined to get away before the first symptoms manifested themselves.

Twenty minutes after his departure, Percy John complained of heartburn, gradually became worse, and was carried up to bed. He was obviously suffering intense pain; he felt, he said, as he had done the previous August when Lamson had given him a pill in the Isle of Wight. He vomited frequently, and during the intervals between these attacks he was in such agony that he was with difficulty kept down by those who were holding him. Asked to describe his symptoms, he declared that his throat was closing and that his skin was being drawn up.

At five minutes to nine, Dr Other Windsor Berry, the practitioner who regularly attended the school, arrived, and at his suggestion Dr Edward Little, who happened to be in the house, also inspected the patient. They applied hot linseed poultices to the stomach and gave the boy white of egg beaten up in water, but without any beneficial results.

Seeing that the pain increased rather than diminished, they injected morphia at about ten o'clock. The symptoms abated somewhat as the drug took effect, but shortly before eleven they returned in an even more aggravated form. A further injection produced no apparent effect, and at twenty minutes past eleven, after four hours of the most exquisite agony, the unfortunate boy died.

That death was due to some irritant poison was the immediate – in fact, the inevitable – theory of both doctors, and they at once collected a sample of the vomit for chemical analysis. On 6 December a post-mortem examination was held by Drs (Thomas) Bond, Little and Berry, but, apart from a slight congestion of one of the lungs, the body proved to be organically healthy and they could discover no natural cause of death.

Having bungled the affair at Shanklin owing to meanness, Lamson erred this time on the side of generosity: there can be no doubt that during his visit he had succeeding in administering an exceptionally large dose of aconitine to his brother-in-law.

What medium he used to convey the poison is uncertain. It was the theory of the prosecution that the fatal dose was contained in the capsule that the boy swallowed, but it will be remembered that Mr Bedbrook was standing at Lamson's elbow and saw him fill the empty shell with castor sugar. Unless the doctor added sleight of hand to his other accomplishments, it is doubtful whether poison could have been introduced to the capsule without Mr Bedbrook noticing.

It seems more probable that the aconitine was contained in the slice of cake which the doctor gave to Percy John. Even though the cake may not already have been cut when Lamson produced it (as I have stated, there appears to be a conflict of opinion on this point), it would have been simple for him, knowing which portion he had impregnated with poison, to give that particular piece to his brother-in-law. The cake was an ordinary Dundee one, supplied by Messrs Buzzards, and all that was needed to transform it into the most certain instrument of death was to extract a few raisins near the surface, to fill them with aconitine, and to replace them, care being taken to leave some distinctive mark, so that no miscarriage of murder might arise.

If this theory be correct, and it was secretly held by counsel defending Lamson, what point could there have been in the capsule incident? That Lamson had thought out the whole performance very carefully is proved by his demand for sugar (which, in spite of his assertion, has the effect of augmenting rather than of counteracting the alcohol in sherry), and by his production of the capsules, which seem to have been bought for that special purpose and to have been introduced into the conversation apropos of nothing at all. Perhaps Lamson wished to distract attention from his real plan. If suspicion of foul play arose, it would naturally be suggested that the poison had been administered in the capsule, and the fact that he had openly filled it with plain sugar right under the eyes of Mr Bedbrook must inevitably be proved in court and might go far towards establishing his plea of Not Guilty. It was an elaborate but not very skilful scheme, and though at the trial the Crown relied solely upon the capsule theory, the precise medium through which the poison was administered did not play a cardinal part in the presentation either of the prosecution or of the defence.

Every circumstance, then, pointed to murder, and to Lamson as the murderer. Who was the last person to give food to the deceased? Who would benefit financially by his death? The police had no great difficulty in reaching the obvious conclusion, and when other incidents were revealed, including the purchase of aconitine a few weeks earlier and the elaborate lies to Tulloch, their suspicions amounted almost to certainty. Lamson's name was freely mentioned in connection with the case, and had he been in England he would at once have been detained. But he had vanished — according to his own account, to Paris, but no one could certainly say whither.

Then it was that Lamson resolved upon a bold and desperate stroke: a stroke at once impudent and imprudent, yet so daring in conception that, had the case against him been less strong, it might have succeeded.

Suddenly, dramatically, he returned to London on 8 December. Going to Scotland Yard, he demanded to see Inspector James Butcher. Questioned as to his business, he replied, 'I am Dr Lamson, whose name has been mentioned in connection with the death at Wimbledon.' He went on to say that he had come back to clear the matter up, and hoped that his return and his explanation would obviate any necessity of preferring an actual charge against him. After reporting his arrival to the authorities, the inspector sat chatting with him upon other topics for an hour or so, and then took him before the competent magistrate.

Lamson's nerve, which had dictated this theatrical and seemingly willing surrender, now began to desert him, and indeed afterwards he never exhibited the courage and self-control that might have been expected from so inhuman a criminal. He apparently anticipated that, owing to his voluntary return, bail would be allowed — but, as is usual in capital cases, his application was refused.

And so, only five days after the commission of the crime, which he had plotted probably for five months, Lamson found himself in custody, from which there could be but one deliverance — for with his education and experience he must have realised that only the miracle, which every human being half-believes will intervene in his favour, could save him from the gallows.

On 9 March 1882, the trial opened at the Central Criminal Court, Old Bailey, before Mr Justice Hawkins. The Solicitor-General, Sir F. Herschel, led for the Crown, and with him were Mr Poland and Mr A. L. Smith. Lamson was represented by Mr Montagu Williams, Mr C. Matthews, Mr E. Gladstone, and Mr W. S. Robson.

An immense crowd had assembled outside the court, and to those who were fortunate enough to be admitted, the prisoner was naturally the centre of interest. His was a face that could not easily be forgotten: a lofty forehead, a pair of dark, restless, intelligent eyes, and a thick black beard of the shape favoured by Charles Dickens — in effect a lean, sinister face, but the face of a thinker and of a man of refinement. He bowed slightly to the judge, and in answer to the indictment pleaded Not Guilty.

The case outlined by the Solicitor-General was an overwhelmingly strong one; the only difficulty experienced by the prosecution was the actual proof of the presence of aconitine in the body of the deceased. At that date it was impossible to detect vegetable poisons by any chemical test, and the only analytical experiment which could be undertaken was that of tasting extracts from the various organs. One cannot but sympathise with the expert, Dr Thomas

Stevenson, over what must have been an extremely unpleasant job.

Drs Little and Berry, who had attended the deceased, could give little more than a description of his death and of the results of the post-morten examination. Both frankly confessed that they knew nothing of the properties of aconitine, and Mr Williams, who had been 'coached' for the case by an eminent toxicologist and was prepared to confute them with his special knowledge, made what capital he could out of their ignorance. It was the theory of the defence that the boy had died from pressure, caused by curvature of the spine, on the arteries, but counsel could not make the doctors commit themselves. They declined to say definitely that death could not have resulted from this cause, yet refused equally to agree that it might have done.

With Dr Bond, who had assisted the local doctors at the post-mortem examination, Mr Williams had no more success. He, like the others, admitted that he was not acquainted with the various preparations of aconitia, and that he had never met a case of poisoning by that drug. It was suggested by the defence that if aconitine was found in the body — minute traces of different poisons are frequently discovered during post-mortem examination of people who have died from other causes — the amount was not sufficient to produce death. Here, like the preceding witnesses, Dr Bond relied upon text-books and personal inexperience.

Mr Williams: 'Would you, supposing death had been occasioned by aconitine, expect to find the amount of poison that had caused death or would it have disappeared?' — 'I believe it would be possible to use so small a dose that it would not be found in the stomach.' (The prisoner, after his experiment in the Isle of Wight, was probably best qualified to elucidate this point.)

'Supposing death caused by aconitine, would you expect to find the actual amount that caused death?' — 'That would depend upon the amount. My opinion is that if death was caused by an ordinary amount, traces would be found.'

'Of the amount that caused death?' — 'Not all.'

The witness went on to explain that the poison would be absorbed by the other organs, but when pressed he had again to admit that he possessed no special knowledge of aconitine.

Mr Williams therefore had to reserve his learning for Dr Stevenson. In examination-in-chief the doctor described the various experiments that he had conducted. From the contents of the bowels he obtained, by Stass's process, an alkaloidal extract 'which was distinctive and produced a very faint sensation like that of aconitia. When placed on the tongue, burning of the lips was produced, though the extract did not touch the lips. Burning, tingling — a kind of numbness peculiar but difficult to define: a salivation creating a desire to expectorate, a sensation at the back of the throat of swelling up, and this was followed by a peculiar seared sensation of the tongue, as if a hot iron had been drawn over it.'

Later, in answer to the judge, he declared that he had between fifty and seventy alkaloids in his possession and had tasted them all. As the symptoms from his experiment with aconitine lasted acutely for over four hours, one can appreciate that Dr Stevenson's job was no sinecure.

The only other test that could be undertaken was the inoculation of mice with extracts from the organs submitted to him. In each case the injections produced precisely the same symptoms and results as an injection with Morson's Aconitia. A considerable number of mice were sacrified in this way, and though Mr Williams in his closing speech condemned the cruelty of these experiments, there can be no doubt that they enormously strengthened the case for the prosecution.

Giving as his opinion that one-sixteenth of a grain of aconitia was a fatal dose, the witness showed how easily even a grain of the poison could be placed in a capsule: by taking it in this way it would be impossible to detect any taste, and the burning of the tongue and lips described by Dr Stevenson would not at once occur. It may, however, be pointed out that the same result would be achieved by filling a raisin skin with the drug. The fact that the cake, when subjected to chemical analysis, revealed no trace of poison, does not dispose of our theory, for had aconitine been administered in the way suggested, it would not have impregnated the whole cake.

The cross-examination of Dr Stevenson was too technical to be of general interest. Though it proved the profound study that Mr Williams had devoted to the case, it failed to shake either the authority of the witness or the strength of the case for the prosecution. It was an ordeal from which few would have emerged with so much credit.

With witnesses as to fact, such as Mr Bedbrook and Mr Tulloch, counsel was slightly more successful. Under the questioning of so skilled an advocate, they were made to contradict themselves over non-essential matters; yet the main outline of the story remained untouched and damning.

One rather curious piece of testimony was that given by the assistants of Messrs Allen & Hanbury's, where it was alleged Lamson had purchased aconitine. On hearing that Lamson's name had been mentioned in connection with the death of Percy John, they recalled that he had visited their shop. Looking up their note of the sale, they came to the conclusion that the drug which he had bought was atropine, which is also a vegetable poison. Later, before there had been any suggestion that aconitine had been discovered in the body of the deceased, they changed their opinion, on account of the price of the drug, and informed the police that the doctor had bought from them two grains of aconitine. Lamson had been in the habit of mixing atropine with morphia for the self-injections in which he indulged, but though Mr Williams pointed out the probability that atropine, not aconitine, had been purchased, the witnesses refused to accept his correction.

For the defence, no evidence was called. The Criminal Evidence Act had not then been passed, and so the prisoner was not considered a competent witness (while, apparently, everyone else who could in any way testify to the facts of the case had already been placed in the box by the prosecution).

Mr Williams was therefore unable to urge the probability of any opposing story, and had to content himself with demonstrating the improbability of the story presented by the Crown. His speech lasted for many hours, and though here and there rather florid and rhetorical, it must rank as one of the most eloquent and moving appeals ever heard in a criminal court — an example of the old school of oratory which has now disappeared. But it was a gallant effort in a hopeless cause. The facts themselves stood out stark and incontrovertible, and he was unable to do more than confuse some of the minor issues. He waxed indignant over Dr Stevenson's treatment of mice; he discovered a scandal in the refusal of the authorities to allow Lamson to be represented at the chemical analysis; he drew a pathetic picture of the prisoner's devoted wife, who, if the jury's verdict were adverse, would be condemned to worse than death.

This was all very fine, but the Solicitor-General's unemotional reply nullified its effect, and by the time Sir Henry Hawkins had finished his dispassionate review of the evidence, Mr Williams's sentimental thunder was almost forgotten. After an absence of three-quarters of an hour, the jury returned a verdict of Guilty, and Lamson, 'protesting his innocence before God,' was sentenced to death.

Strenuous efforts to save him were now made by friends both in England and America, and the fact that they should have rallied round him in this crisis proves that there must have been something likeable about the man. That so charming a companion could commit so appalling a crime argued insanity. Affidavits, covering a number of years, were filed to show that Lamson's brain had for a long time been abnormal, and that his addiction to the morphine habit had destroyed his ethical sense and left him defence-less against a homicidal impulse.

One of the most illuminating of the documents was sworn by a comrade of Lamson's who had served with him at Bukarest during the Balkan War of 1877. Whilst there, 'he exhibited a mania for the administration of aconitine in almost every case, using it in season and out of season, and in such quantities as to alarm the medical staff and render his recall to England necessary'. Another affidavit dealt with his conduct at the siege of Paris in 1871, where his reckless use of drugs made him a public danger; while from America came a declaration signed by three eminent doctors, who had met him the previous summer (1881), to the effect that morphine injections had undoubtedly turned his brain: 'He passed the greater part of the day either dozing or attempting to read. He was then using a mixture apparently of morphia and atropine, but said that he preferred aconitine but could not procure it in that section of the country.' Dr Gustavus Winston, the medical director of the New York Mutual Life Assurance Company, considered that 'he had become a helpless victim of the habit, which had seriously impaired his mental powers and destroyed his moral responsibility'.

Other persons tried to prove that he was tainted with hereditary insanity from the fact that his grandmother had been an inmate of the New York Bloomingdale Asylum — but as she was not removed there until the age of seventy-six, this was not very cogent testimony.

Lastly, his solicitor deposed that 'he could obtain no assistance from him in the preparation of his defence — that he appeared to have no memory and to be incapable of appreciating the bearing of any of the facts of his case or of the gravity of his position!'

In deference to this universal clamour, the Home Secretary, Sir William Harcourt, postponed the date of the execution in order that the affidavits might be considered. A further respite was granted at the request of President Chester Arthur to allow the documents from America to reach their destination. But after perusing them, Sir William found himself unable to recommend the Queen to

55

exercise her prerogative of mercy; nor can there be any doubt that he was right. The defence of insanity had not been raised at the trial, and even had it been urged with all the eloquence at Mr William's command, it is inconceivable that the jury would have returned a different verdict. The burden of proving insanity rests, of course, upon the defence, and it must be established that the state of the prisoner's mind was such that he could not realise the nature and quality of his acts. How could this be said of Lamson, who must have appreciated the pecuniary benefit he would derive from the death of Percy John? Or, if it be suggested that the crime was the result of homicidal mania, why should he have selected this victim? The motive for the murder was too convincing to support a plea of insanity.

The execution was ultimately fixed for Friday, 28 April, nearly six weeks after the conviction, and the well-meant efforts of his friends to win a reprieve served only to aggravate the prisoner's anguish. Fear rather than remorse dominated him, and his mental agony must have been in proportion to the physical suffering he had inflicted upon his victim. Courage and comfort he could find only in the morphia-needle, and the reaction, resulting from his inability to secure the drug in prison, completely prostrated him. One moment he seemed oblivious of what awaited him; the next, knowledge returned with redoubled terror.

A few days before his execution, he wrote a long rambling document which appears to be an admission of his guilt, and he also made a verbal confession to the chaplain: but he denied upon oath that he was in any way responsible for the death of Herbert John, and it may be that the world, loath to believe that any murderer is ever hanged for his first murder, is in this instance mistaken.

It was not to be expected that he would meet his end with fortitude. Here was no stoic, but a poor, weak soul, appalled at the prospect of death. Realising upon that fatal morning that his time had come, he abandoned all effort at composure and was helped, almost unconscious, to the scaffold. There, unable to stand, he was held upon the drop by two warders. Even as the hangman was pulling the lever, he tried to snatch another minute of life by begging the chaplain to recite just one more prayer.

Had he been tried today, when the criminal code is administered by Harley Street, he might have escaped the consequences of his crime. Of the fact that he was not altogether normal there is abundant evidence; but who has a brain so nice that it can apportion responsibility between morphia, poverty, desperation, and chance?

The Murder of Marilyn

JOAN LOCK

THE BELIEF THAT doctors are 'respectable', together with their privileged status within the community and, on occasion, the unwitting complicity of their peers, has certainly allowed some of them to get away with murder. But in one case at least, the presumption by a doctor that he was fire-proof, and the hubris which this attitude engendered, rebounded on him with a vengeance.

Back in the early 1950s, the tall, handsome Dr Sam Sheppard, neurosurgeon and osteopath, had not only his own medical status to protect him but also that of his wealthy and influential family. His father and two elder brothers were signatories of the Hippocratic oath, and the Sheppards ran their own hospital, Bay View, near Cleveland, Ohio. When Sam got into trouble, the family instantly rallied round and behaved with what in retrospect certainly looks like arrogance.

'Dr Sam' and his attractive wife Marilyn seemed to have everything; wealth, position, a full social and sporting life, a loved seven-year-old son, and another child on the way. Then, in the early hours of Sunday, 4 July 1954 – Independence Day – the bubble burst.

On the previous evening, this gilded pair had entertained another couple to dinner at their colonial-style house perched on a cliff-top overlooking Lake Erie. After dinner, while the others watched a movie on television, Sam fell asleep on the couch. Nothing surprising in that, for he was known for his ability to drop off at will. He had had a

58

heavy day, and the next was likely to be equally busy as the Sheppards had invited a number of their many friends to a patriotic barbeque on their lawn.

Sam Sheppard was still asleep when, just after midnight, the other couple left. What followed remains a matter of conjecture. According to Sam, he was woken by his wife's screams for help — he ran upstairs to their bedroom, where he saw 'a white form' standing over Marilyn's bed — he grappled with the intruder — then a blow from behind knocked him unconscious.

When he came to, he found that his wife had been battered to death by, it was later estimated, thirty-five blows to the head with a heavy instrument. He ran into his son's bedroom but found him safe; sound asleep. Then hearing a noise from the ground floor, he dashed downstairs, where he caught a glimpse of what appeared to be a man with bushy hair disappearing through the rear door and down the steps to the beach. Dr Sam gave chase; once more, this very athletic doctor tackled his quarry but was knocked unconscious. He came to again just before dawn; he was lying half in and half out of the lake. Back at the house, he phoned a friend, John Spencer Houk, the mayor of Bay Village, yelling 'For God's sake, Spen, come quick. I think they've killed Marilyn.'

That was at 5.45 am. Though the Houks lived only a hundred yards away, they took about ten minutes to arrive — by car. They found Sheppard sitting in his ground-floor den. He was naked from the waist up and nursing an injured neck. His face was bruised, his trousers wet, his manner dazed. Mrs Houk went up alone to see the body. Seven minutes later, the first policeman arrived. A further seven minutes after that, the first Sheppard brother came in, followed shortly afterwards by the second. They examined Sam, and at half-past six, only three-quarters of an hour after the phone call to Houk, they were ushering him out of the house past the gathering police and on to their hospital for treatment. They asked permission from no one to do this — but, they subsequently claimed, the police did not object.

Later, accusations that Sam had been whisked away and given sanctuary from police questioning were countered by his allies, who pointed out that the police *did* question him at the hospital — for ten minutes at 9 am, for twenty minutes at 11 am, and for no more than half an hour at 3 pm. But that is very limited questioning in a murder case, and it is disingenuous of reporter Paul Holmes, in his book *The Sheppard Murder Case*, to state: 'Sam got no sanctuary in the hospital.' Sheppard may not, in fact, have been thought ill enough to be admitted to hospital by any authority other than his family: whether he was or was not was always disputed. A GP who examined him on behalf of the coroner said that his injuries were superficial, while a neurosurgeon, subsequently called in by the Sheppards, disagreed.

But, in any event, there is no doubt that one feels more secure on one's own ground — no doubt, either, that if Sam needed time to hone his story, he was given it. What's more, his family quickly had him under sedation (later, there were objections about statements made by him when he was drowsy being used as evidence) and, according to the police, one brother actually interrupted a brief interrogation no fewer than four times. Sam also refused to take a lie-detector or truth-serum test — on the advice, it was claimed, of his lawyers.

The protective ploys, if that was what they were, at first appeared to work, even though both the coroner and the police made no bones about being extremely suspicious of Sam's story. There *were* signs of a burglary — drawers pulled out and their contents scattered, a medical bag emptied on the floor — yet nothing was taken except one phial of morphine. It was odd that he had stayed so long asleep downstairs — usually one gets chilly and uncomfortable, wakes and goes to bed. He had been wearing a corduroy jacket over a T-shirt when he went to sleep; the jacket was found folded on or by the couch where he had slept, but there was no sign of the T-shirt. Perhaps the murderer had pulled it off to replace his own heavily bloodstained shirt, Sam suggested. There were surprisingly few fingerprints, and none that was 'foreign' to the house — suggesting some time-consuming wiping-clean to imply that a burglary had taken place. (Of course, it was possible that a burglar had done just that.) It seemed odd that the Sheppards' son had slept through all the commotions — and odder still that their dog had stayed as quiet as a mouse. There were rumours that Dr Sam had a girlfriend, a laboratory technician named Susan Hayes, and had recently been to California to see her — but he vehemently denied them at the inquest.

As is often so when a multiplicity of agencies is involved (in the Sheppard case, the Cleveland Police and the local force; coroner's, sheriff's and prosecutor's offices), the conduct of the investigation was haphazard. The frustrations of the investigators were soon picked up by newspaper reporters, particularly those of the *Cleveland Press*, which eventually abandoned merely hinting that the influential Sheppards were obstructing justice, and came straight out with headlines such as 'Why Isn't Sam Sheppard in Jail?' and 'Quit Stalling — Bring Him In.' Eventually, on 30 July, twenty-six days after Marilyn was murdered, the police did so and charged him with the crime.

The trial, which drew immense media attention, was long and complex and, according to some, left more questions open than answered. Questions about the murder-weapon and bloodstains, for example. The coroner testified that a bloody mark on Marilyn's pillow was the imprint of a surgical implement used to bludgeon her — but failed to identify the implement. The lack of blood on Sheppard's clothing (only one patch on his trousers — which, he claimed, was the result of bending over Marilyn to take her pulse after finding her body) was also much debated. The prosecution said he had got rid of his heavily-stained T-shirt and probably wasn't wearing trousers anyway. There was also much confusing evidence about the distribution of blood in the murder room and argument over the surprisingly light blood trail (seven unidentifiable spots) outside.

It was at a late stage of the trial that the prosecution dropped their bombshell. Till then, rumours had abounded that the defendant was an enthusiastic Lothario, but the police had been unable to substantiate any of them — save that regarding Susan Hayes, the involvement he had denied at the inquest.

The slim, suntanned, twenty-four-year-old Miss Hayes appeared on the witness-stand wearing what a reporter described as 'the standard wardrobe for females in murder trials' — a demure black dress with a prim white Peter Pan collar. She and Dr Sam had been having an affair for a year and a half, she said. It had begun when she, working at the Bay View hospital, had been given lifts home by this handsome youngest son of the partnership. Susan had moved to California several months before the murder, but meanwhile she had met Sam illicitly when he attended an osteopathic convention out west. Dr Sam, Susan claimed, had told her that he was considering divorce — a claim vigorously denied by the defendant when he took the stand. He did, however, while refusing to name names, confess to other extra-marital affairs, but declared that he had always told his wife about them — 'I didn't want her to hear about them from other people'. This confession of multi-adultery could, of course, merely have been a way of making the Hayes liaison seem less significant — so not a motive for murder. He also admitted that Marilyn and he were having sexual problems; since the birth of their son Chip seven years earlier, he told the jury, Marilyn had 'lost her sexual aggressiveness'.

The trial lasted for nine weeks, and the jury were out for a further five days before they found Dr Sam not guilty of first-degree murder. The shouts of triumph uttered by his family soon died as he was found guilty of murder in the second degree — though this at least meant that he was no longer a candidate for the electric chair.

Dr Sam was sentenced to life imprisonment — which, in

effect, meant that it would be ten years before parole would be considered. But while he was awaiting transfer to the Ohio State Penitentiary, other family tragedies occurred. Within a month of his conviction, Sam's mother shot herself; eleven days later his father died of a haemorrhage due to a recently-diagnosed cancer of the stomach. The prisoner was promptly placed in a bare 'anti-suicide' cell.

The fight to free Sheppard developed into a long-running saga. When all of the possible legal moves had been made, his brothers applied to the 'Court of Last Resort', an organisation set up by the crime novelist, Erle Stanley Gardner, to investigate cases in which there seemed to be some doubt as to whether justice had been done. Under the auspices of the pseudo court, the Sheppard brothers and their wives (some or all of whom, it had often been implied, had guilty knowledge and had attempted to obstruct the police and coroner) offered to submit to a lie-detector test. They passed with flying colours, but when Sam volunteered to take the test, the necessary permission was withheld. Then, suddenly, in June 1957, there was a new development. Another man confessed to having committed the murder.

Twenty-three-year-old Donald Wedler, an inmate of a Florida prison, told the authorities that on the night of 3 July 1954 he, 'doped up' on heroin, had stolen a car in which he drove to Bay Village, where he had broken into a house and committed the murder: that he was, in fact, the 'bushy haired intruder'. (At the trial, two defence witnesses had claimed to have seen such a person lurking near the Sheppard residence that night, but there was an understandable suspicion that the Sheppards' offer of a $10,000 reward had affected their memories.)

Erle Stanley Gardner arranged for Wedler to take a lie-detector test. The polygraph operator concluded that either Wedler had done the deed or sincerely believed that he had, but the Cleveland police, finding discrepancies between his tale and Sam's version, were convinced that his confession was a hoax. Shortly afterwards, Sam's elderly lawyer died, and the publicity-loving whizz-kid attorney F. Lee Bailey, took over. He pressed hard for Sam to be allowed to take lie-detector and truth-drug tests, but was refused; then he unsuccessfully pleaded before the State Pardon and Parole Commission for, *inter alia*, alteration of the verdict to manslaughter; then, but again without success, he made habeas-corpus petitions to State and Federal Courts on the ground that Dr Sam had been denied his civil rights due to errors of law and procedure in the conduct of the trial.

Eventually Bailey did get Sheppard out — but only after he had served ten years and was eligible for parole consideration anyway. A federal judge decided that the conduct of the trial had violated the defendant's constitutional rights on several counts; and, after making some cutting comments about the carnival atmosphere surrounding the trial, and the 'massive, pervasive and prejudicial publicity', the judge ordered that a retrial was to take place within sixty days. Shortly before Sheppard was released on remand, Marilyn's father killed himself with a shotgun, leaving a note saying that he was 'sick of everything'.

One of Dr Sam's first actions was to marry Ariane Tebbenjohanns, a wealthy German divorcee (and half-sister of the wife of Dr Joseph Goebbels) who had been corresponding with him for the past five years. She had become interested in the case when she read about it in a magazine in her dentist's waiting room in Düsseldorf, and before long was convinced that Dr Sam had been wrongly convicted.

There were further delays before, on 16 November 1966 — over twelve years after the murder — a second Cleveland jury found the defendant Not Guilty. That verdict seems to have been based wholly or largely on apparent discrepancies in police and forensic evidence.

Freedom did not bring happiness, however. Sheppard was heavily in debt to F. Lee Bailey, who had been representing him without payment for several years, and his medical licence was not restored for a considerable time. Within a year of his reinstatement, he and the hospital in which he was then working, the Youngstown Osteopathic in Ohio, were sued for negligence following the deaths of two of his surgical patients. The hospital's insurance company insisted on Sam's resignation. The day after he had submitted it, Ariane not only sued for divorce but also obtained a restraining order against Sam, who, she claimed had often threatened her.

This loquacious German lady, who had donated a great deal of her own money to the defence fund, complained to the press that Sam habitually carried a pistol, knives and a hatchet (presumably not all at once, else he would have bulged rather suspiciously). Not finished yet, she said that he had stolen from her, was subject to extreme changes of mood, and had told her he no longer needed her as he had a new girl-friend.

Unable to practise surgery without insurance, Dr Sam set up as a GP, and, always a keep-fit fanatic, took up all-in wrestling, contributing his purses to cancer research. Shortly afterwards, he married Colleen Strickland, his trainer's nineteen-year-old daughter, and moved in with her family. His relationship with his own family had deteriorated since his release, though he did occasionally see his son.

Dr Sam died in April 1970, after collapsing and refusing to allow his in-laws to call a doctor. His death was ascribed to liver failure — possibly due to heavy drinking.

When I first read Sam's version of what happened on that fateful night, my reaction was of the ho-hum sort; and his flashy behaviour following his release certainly indicates an unstable character. But doubts crept in later, just as they did with several of those closely involved with the case. Maybe he didn't do it. Some of the evidence against him was flimsy, some may have been fabricated or perverted; if he *was* innocent, his long martyrdom may well have made him unstable.

However, on balance, I think he did murder Marilyn. Possibly in a frenzy when she rejected his sexual advances or refused him a divorce. Why would an intruder have beaten Marilyn so ferociously and so many times? How could he have struck so many blows before Sam arrived? Why was the son not woken by any of the various loud noises? What happened to the T-shirt? And, of course, there is the question that Sherlock Holmes would undoubtedly have asked: Why did the dog not bark in the night?

Postscript

From the *New York Times*, 14 August 1989:

> BAY VILLAGE, Ohio — It is not hard to understand the fascination in this quiet Cleveland suburb with the murder of the pregnant wife of a local doctor, Dr Samuel H. Sheppard — even if it did happen thirty-five years ago....
>
> Yet another theory of the crime emerged a few weeks ago out of another murder trial in nearby Lakewood. Richard Eberling, fifty-nine years old, a window-washer, part-time handyman and occasional interior decorator, was found guilty on 7 July of murdering a wealthy ninety-year-old Lakewood widow and forging her will with the help of his long-time companion Oscar (Obie) B. Henderson. It seems Mr Eberling wooed the widow's confidence for at lease twenty years — becoming the principal person taking care of her when she died....
>
> Quick to follow the trial was the resurrection of Mr Eberling's connection to the Sheppard case: He had been employed as a window-washer by the Sheppards; he admitted to being in the bedroom to clean windows just two days before the murder; blood of his type was discovered inside the home, which he explained at the time as having resulted from a cut while he was working....
>
> Relatives of Dr Sheppard have called for the three-decade-old murder case to be reopened.... But the Bay Village police say no new evidence has come to light....

The Fatal Gambles of William Palmer

THE REVEREND EVELYN BURNABY*

*Sometime Rector of Burrough-on-the-Hill, Leicestershire, Evelyn Burnaby was a member of a family that claimed to be the oldest in that county. His mother lived to be over a hundred; one of his sisters, Mrs Manners-Sutton, was considered by many of her mid-nineteenth-century contemporaries to be the most beautiful woman of the age; his brother, Colonel Fred Burnaby, commander of a regiment of Horse Guards, was reckoned to be the strongest man in the British Army. (A pen-portrayer of Evelyn, speaking in passing of Fred, noted that he once 'carried a pony under each arm up the stairs of the cavalry barracks at Windsor.... Colonel Burnaby made a successful trip in a balloon across the Channel – alone and with only a biscuit and a bottle of Apollinaris for sustenance.') The Reverend Evelyn explained that his fascination with criminal trials was seeded in his pre-Eton childhood, while he was living in Bedfordshire: 'My first appearance in a Crown Court was at the Spring Assizes of 1856, when I was taken by my mother to hear three cases tried before Mr Justice Cresswell in the old Shire Hall, facing St Paul's Church, and adjoining the old Grammar School at Bedford. It was here that Lord Brampton [better known as Sir Henry Hawkins – and still better known as "The Hanging Judge"] was educated [also, for about seven years till 1909, Ronald True – the maniac who in 1922 murdered a London prostitute whose business-name was Olive Young].

From that moment I took a keen interest in the law courts, and the acquaintance of my family with my dear old friend, Mr Justice Wightman, helped to increase that interest. Many a time I have sat by him when he was trying cases, and as a lad I accompanied him on the old Norfolk circuit. It was a pleasure to me to attend the Old Bailey Sessions and listen to the speeches of famous advocates engaged on either side, and note the gradual unfolding of the evidence — generally circumstantial — at the same time gathering an insight into the extraordinary and marvellous combination of good and evil in the characters of real drama, for I have never yet met a criminal in whom there was not some inherent good.'

MY RECOLLECTION goes back to the trial at the Old Bailey in 1856 of Palmer, the poisoner, who was arraigned before the Lord Chief Justice of England (Lord Campbell), Mr Baron Alderson and Mr Justice Cresswell for the murder of John Parsons Cook. A host of counsel appeared for the Crown on the one hand, and for the defence on the other. Sir Alexander Cockburn, then Attorney-General, led for the Crown, and had studied chemistry for three months previously so that he might be able to test the value of the evidence of the various medical experts who were called on either side. And with him was Mr Edwin James, who, at that time, seemed to have a career of brilliancy before him unsurpassed; but recklessness and an array of unforeseen circumstances cast him down from the pedestal he ought to have occupied. The juniors for the Crown were — if my memory serves me right — Mr Bodkin and Mr Huddlestone. Palmer had secured as his leading counsel a famous advocate in the person of Mr Serjeant Shee, whose speech for the defence occupied no fewer than eight hours, and the learned counsel was so carried away by his feelings that he was called to order by the Chief Justice when, in the heat of his argument, he assured the jury on his own word of honour that his client was innocent of the murder.

Amongst the leading experts for the Crown was Dr

Alfred Swayne Taylor, author of the standard work on medical jurisprudence. I remember very well sitting with him alone on the Bench of the New Court at the bewitching midnight hour when the jury had been deliberating for three hours in a case of murder. Dr Taylor had been a witness and subjected to severe cross-examination, and confided to me that he wished he had never written his book. 'Because,' he explained, 'they make me say something in the witness box and then put in that confounded book to contradict me.'

The strongest witness for the prisoner was Dr Benjamin Ward Richardson (who was afterwards knighted); he was a dear old friend of mind, a native of my own village of Somerby in Leicestershire, and had received his early education at my old home at Burrough-on-the-Hill from the Rev J. Y. Nutt, father of Mr Alfred Nutt, the architect to the King at Windsor Castle. Dr Richardson, a strict temperance man, received a bequest from Sir Charles Trevelyan of a large cellar of wine which was to be used for scientific purposes. I begged in vain for him to give me a bottle of Tokay, but the doctor told me that he meant to carry out the terms of the bequest by trying to find out what caused the aroma in the wine, and that as soon as he found it out he would throw away the contents of the cellar.

Dr Richardson suggested a very clever but somewhat untenable idea that angina pectoris might have been the cause of Cook's death. He quoted a similar case, but on cross-examination was bound to confess that, although the symptoms were similar in both cases, he had not analysed for strychnine when making the post-mortem on the death of the patient where the latter had died from angina pectoris. There was a conflict of evidence at Palmer's trial as to whether death was caused by strychnine or not, the issue to the jury being, 'Death by strychnine or not guilty', and I have often doubted very much whether Palmer ought ever to have been convicted, inasmuch as there was a conflict of medical evidence as to whether the amount of strychnine found in the body was sufficient to cause Cook's death. It was probably due to Sir Alexander Cockburn's closing speech for the Crown that Palmer owed his conviction, and that great lawyer is reported to have said that the best compliment ever paid to him in his life was that given to him by Palmer in the dock, when the jury had returned a verdict of Guilty: the convicted man threw over a strip of paper to his solicitor, Mr Smith, in the well of the court, with these words on it, 'It was not the horse, but the riding that did it,' alluding in sporting language to the effective manner in which Sir Alexander Cockburn had conducted the case for the prosecution.

It may be interesting to interpolate here a brief history of Palmer's remarkable career which culminated in the murder of John Parsons Cook. The latter was the owner of a racehorse, Polestar, whose wonderful series of victories on the turf in 1855 attracted particularly the notice of William Palmer, who took the earliest opportunity of making the acquaintance of Cook. The two soon became closely intimate, visiting race meetings together all over the country. Palmer, then about thirty years of age, was a medical man who had been in practice at the little town of Rugeley in Staffordshire. The turf, however, had more attractions for him than medicine, so he made his practice over to a former assistant and took to horse-racing for a living. He was very soon in dire straits for money, and to get it made his first lapse into crime by forging the name of his mother, who was possessed of considerable property, to an acceptance. In order that this should not be discovered, it was necessary that he must needs go further. Palmer did not hesitate, but very adroitly covered one forgery with another. There were many promissory notes in his name falling due, and just when he was becoming sorely pressed, his wife died very suddenly after being seized with sickness, followed by convulsions. He had insured her life to the extent of £13,000, and this put him right for a time and enabled him to purchase two racehorses. But luck was against him both as an owner and as a backer, and he then resorted to borrowing money from his friend Cook.

Though the latter never knew it, Palmer forged his name to a cheque. Just when there was likely to be trouble about the cheque and other monetary transactions, Palmer was once more relieved through the medium of his brother's death, also from sickness and convulsions, and whom he had insured for a large amount. This time the insurance office made considerable demur about paying and hinted at the strangeness of the death; but nothing could be proved, and eventually the money was paid over to him, only to go the way of former sums. After a time, certain bill-discounters who held forged acceptances and promissory notes began to threaten action. Palmer, casting about for a way out of his difficulties, saw it once more in his 'friend', John Parsons Cook.

The latter's horse — Polestar — was entered for Shrewsbury Races on 14 November 1885, and the two intimates travelled to the town together and put up at the same hotel, the Raven, where the tragedy began. On the evening of the races they were drinking together, and Cook pressed Palmer to have some more brandy. 'Not unless you finish your glass,' was the answer. Cook, seeing he had left a fair quantity, swallowed it at a gulp and directly afterwards complained that it had burnt his throat.

That night he was seized with violent sickness and a doctor was called in; the medicine afforded relief and, the vomiting having ceased, Cook was able to accompany Palmer next morning to Rugeley, where he had engaged rooms in an hotel directly opposite Palmer's house. Here he was again seized with violent sickness, which occurred directly after Palmer had been dining with him. The illness became worse, and Palmer, being his close and constant attendant, took advantage of Cook's prostrate condition to pocket the proceeds of the Shrewsbury Race settling. The last act was now at hand. The fraud had to be covered, and from a medical man Palmer procured some strychnine, and the same evening Cook was seized with horrible convulsions and suffered intense pain. Palmer came to his assistance, and the attack — as it was evidently intended to do — passed off, but left the victim terribly weak and ill.

Next day Palmer purchased more strychnine from a chemist in Rugeley. Then he called in two other medical men to see Cook, explaining that the patient had for a long time been sick, and getting them to ascribe the sudden convulsions of the previous day to weakness. They fell in with this view and ordered some tonic pills, which Palmer undertook to see properly administered.

That night two pills were given by Palmer to Cook, who was shortly afterwards seized with agonising convulsions. Palmer was again fetched to his assistance, and at once gave him some more medicine. Cook died twenty minutes later.

The unfortunate young man's relatives were summoned to Rugeley, and to their surprise were told that Palmer held a claim of £4000 against Cook's estate. This aroused strong suspicions, and eventually a post-mortem examination of the deceased's body was ordered.

Besides Palmer's financial difficulties, there were several points of circumstantial evidence tending to prove his guilt as the poisoner of Cook. The fact of his trying to bribe the coroner by a present of game; his attempt to upset the jar which, carefully sealed down, contained the contents of Cook's stomach and which were going to be sent up to London for analysis by experts; and his attempt to bribe the post-boy to upset the mail-cart which carried the jar. All these facts formed links in a chain of circumstantial evidence which required a Caesar in advocacy to resist. Were it not for the circumstantial evidence, crimes must often go undetected, for a man who intends to commit a great crime takes care that if possible no human eye shall be a witness of his act. Men may lie, and do lie, when they testify to actually witnessing a crime, but a watch, and a blood-stain, and a bullet corresponding to those used in a revolver in the possession of a prisoner all supply evidence clear, distinct and conclusive. As in Palmer's case, it becomes a question not of the balance of probabilities but of proof positive — admitting of not the shadow of a doubt.

Whether Palmer poisoned Cook by strychnine or not, Cockburn wove round him a web so complete and perfect that no counsel could extricate the prisoner.

I can distinctly recall the words of the sentence of death. The court at the Old Bailey was packed to overflowing as the jury, after their names had been called out, pronounced their verdict of Guilty. Lord Campbell, having assumed the black cap, thus addressed the prisoner:

> William Palmer, after a long and impartial trial you have been found guilty by a jury of your own countrymen of the crime of wilful murder, and with that verdict I and my learned brothers, who so anxiously have watched this case, entirely concur, and we think the conviction altogether satisfactory. Whether this is the only crime of its kind committed by you is best known to God and your own conscience. I do not wish to harrow your feelings by any reference to it. You have been brought to this court by special Act of Parliament because of the prejudice which existed against you in the county of Stafford, but for the sake of example, the sentence should be carried out where the crime was committed.

The Lord Chief Justice then pronounced the sentence of death in the usual form, and he and the other judges signed the warrant for the removal of the prisoner to the county gaol at Stafford. The convict, with a strong escort of warders, was that same night transported north on the mail train. On alighting from the railway carriage at Stafford, Palmer blithely remarked, 'They seem to have had more rain here than they have had in London!'

The story goes that the inhabitants of Rugeley, finding that their town had achieved an unenviable notoriety through the crime, sought Prime Minister Palmerston's assistance to effect a change of its name. His reply to their petition was prompt and characteristic: 'Yes, of course — by all means call it after me.' The idea was dropped.

Palmer, just before his execution on 27 May 1856, at

By Electric Telegraph.

TRIAL

And Sentence of Death

Passed this Day, May 28th, 1856 on

W. PALMER,

FOR THE

Wilful Murder

Of JOHN PARSONS COOK

At Rugeley, Staffordshire.

MONDAY.

The trial of William Palmer was resumed this morning at the Central Criminal Court. Intense interest was felt as to the result of the trial, it being known that Lord Campbell would sum up the evidence, and the probability of the jury returning their verdict almost immediately following its conclusion

Their lordships, Lord Chief Justice Campbell, Mr. Justice Creswell, and Mr Baron Alderson took their seats on the bench precisely at 10 o'clock, accompanied by the Recorder, Deputy-Recorder, and several of the Aldermen. The Earl of Derby and the Right Hon. W, E. Gladstone were also on the bench.

The crown was represented to-day by only Mr. James, Q.C., Mr. Bodkin, and Mr. Huddlestone ; but the four counsel for the prisoner were all present—viz., Mr. Sergeant Shee, Mr. Grove, Q.C., Mr. Kenealey, and Mr. Gray.

On their lordships taking their seats, the prisoner appeared in the dock, and walked to the bar dressed as on each former occasion, in black with black kid gloves Shortly after entering the dock the prisoner seemed to give himself up to inward thought. Suddenly, however, he awoke from this apparent reverie ; the Lord Chief Justice had begun his charge, and it was quite painful to watch the eagerness with which he prisoner devoured every word. He gazed with a fixed look at his lordship, and appeared nervously apprehensive of losing any portion of the address. In this way he eyed the judge with parted lips until his lordship began to read the evidence, and then he seemed to breath freely again and to look on with comparatively calm indifference.

Before Lord Campbell commenced the summing up Mr Serjeant Shee applied to be allowed to put in an acceptance for £500, drawn by Palmer and accepted by Cook, dated Sept. 1855, which was granted.

> **TUESDAY,**
>
> This morning the summing up of the Learned Judge, was again resumed. His lordship went carefully through the evidence for the defence commenting on each point that seemed material for or against the prisoner, who maintained the same firmness and composure that he exhibited on the Learned Judge commencing his address: his lordship after carefully revising every particle of the testimony that was urged in favour of the prisoner, concluded by telling the Jury that the case was now in their hands, that they would do their duty without fear or favour and return such a verdict as would satisfy their conscience, their God, and their Country.
>
> The Lord Chief Justice having concluded his summing up, the jury retired to consider their verdict, and after an absence of some time returned with a verdict of **GUILTY.** The colour forsook the countenance of Palmer for an instant, but he did not appear to lose his self-possession; and during the delivery of the sentence, when there was scarcely a dry eye in the court, and the utterance of the Lord Chief Justice was at times stifled with emotion, the prisoner stood firm and upright in the dock
>
> The execution of the Prisoner is take place in front of Stafford County Gaol.
>
> R. Astill, Printer, Coventry

Stafford, was asked by the Governor, 'Did you poison Cook?' The answer was, 'I did not poison him by strychnine.' The Governor replied, 'This is no time for quibbling; did you poison him at all?' Palmer said, 'Lord Campbell summed up for death by strychnine. I deny the justice of my sentence. They are my murderers.'

I myself have always thought that Palmer poisoned Cook by antimony, and that minute doses of strychnine were given towards the end to complete the work.

Postscript

From *The Reminiscences of Sir Henry Hawkins, Baron Brampton* (Arnold, London, 1904):

> I was travelling one day on circuit from London to Norwich, and I could not help overhearing the conversation between two fellow-travellers, who were bookmakers returning from the races.
>
> One of the men in the railway-carriage I knew by sight. His name was Kirby — a rough, good-natured, honest sort of man, I believe, as anyone in a small way

of book-making of that day. His companion was a stranger. Everybody at that time talked of Palmer the Rugeley poisoner, for he had just been hanged.

'Bill,' said Kirby, 'I knowed that there Palmer; did *you*?'

'No,' said Bill, 'don't know as ever I did.'

'Well, I had dealings with him, and a nice sort of fellow he was, only nobody never could get any money from him.' After a pause he continued: 'Well, he owed me a matter o' five-and-twenty pound, and I wrote, I suppose, a dozen letters to him, perhaps more; but it was no good, and so at last I sent him a stinger. I knowed what to say to him, for I had 'eeard a bit from the ostler at the public where I stopped. He told me as Palmer persuaded him to let him insure his life, which the fool did, and next time he see Palmer the doctor gave him a drink that nearly made old Sam kick the bucket there and then.

'After I sent the letter, Palmer asked me to come over one day and he'd settle with me. So over I goes, and when I gets to his house was asked into a little room, and left there by myself for a goodish while. On the table was a decanter of sherry wine and a glass. I was putty thirsty, of course, but I didn't touch the wine. Howsomever, there it was to help myself if I'd a mind to. Presently in comes the doctor with a pleasant smile, a friendly shake of the hand, and a "Very glad to see you, Kirby! How are you getting on, Kirby? A glass o' sherry, Kirby? It will do you good after your walk."

' "I shall be glad to have one, Mr Palmer, if you'll join me," I ses, for a thought come to me about Sam the ostler.

"No," he says, "thankee, Kirby, I never drink sherry."

' "No more don't I, Mr Palmer," I ses; and then I asked him if it was agreeable to him to pay what he owed.'

' "No," says he, "Kirby, it is not quite agreeable at present – but – are you quite sure you won't take a glass of sherry, Kirby?"'

' "Quite, sir" I ses, "thankee all the same; I ain't no sherry drinker, Mr Palmer." '

' "What *will* you take?" ses he; "you must have something." '

' "No sir, thankee, my little account's all I wants." '

' "Well, if you won't take anything," ses he, "you may as well have a look round my little farm. I've got some nice pigs to show you." '

'Well, when we got to the sty, there was as nice a farrer as you could see.'

' "I'll tell you what it is, Kirby," ses he: "you've been very good lettin' that little account of ours stand over, and I'll make you a present of one of these sucking-pigs, and my cook shall send him over all ready for roasting." '

' "No, thankee, sir," I ses again; "I ain't come for no pigs." *I worn't goin' to have his damned sherry and poisoned pig.*'

Such was Kirby's story, and I have no doubt he was doomed to death by Palmer. Some time after, when I was a Judge and at the Stafford Assizes, I was talking with Major Talford, the governor of the gaol where Palmer was hanged, and he told me that Palmer talked freely about his case while waiting execution; that he said all through the trial he expected an acquittal, and even after the Judge's terrible summing up, hope did not desert him. 'But,' he added, 'when the jury returned into court, and I saw the cocked-up nose of the perky little foreman, I knew it was a gooser with me.'

On the morning of the execution, the path from the condemned cell to the gallows was wet and muddy, it having rained during the night, and Palmer minced along like a delicate schoolgirl, picking his way and avoiding the puddles. He was particularly anxious not to get his feet wet.

The Smethurst Case

RICHARD D. ALTICK

WILLIAM PALMER was executed on 14 June 1856. Three years later, another doctor was in Newgate awaiting trial on a like charge.

Dr Thomas Smethurst, who had retired from the profession at least six years before he got into his great trouble, had been married since 1828 to a lady twenty or twenty-six years his senior (the evidence is conflicting). In 1858, while they were living in lodgings in Bayswater, West London, he took up with a fellow-lodger, a spinster in her early forties named Isabella Bankes. Miss Bankes was evicted from the house because of her excessive familiarity with the doctor, but he followed her, bigamously married her, and settled down with her in Richmond. In his statement to the court after he was convicted of murdering Miss Bankes, Smethurst explained the second marriage in this somewhat cloudy language:

> It is true that we united ourselves illegally, but it was for a permanency; and the marriage took place in this way: At the request of the deceased — she was a person of property and good family connections, she knew that I was married — and, in order that she should be protected from reproach hereafter, this marriage was preliminary to one at a future period, in the event of my wife dying — she is now seventy-four years of age; therefore, it was fully intended that our union should be of a permanent nature.

But it was fated not to be of a permanent nature. Less

than four months after her marriage, the new Mrs Smethurst took sick with symptoms generally resembling those of acute dysentery, and only a little more than two months later, she died. The attending doctors had strong suspicions that something was amiss; furthermore, it transpired that Smethurst was the beneficiary of his late wife's newly made will. He was therefore charged with murder and brought to trial at the Old Bailey.

Things went badly from the outset. A juror was taken seriously ill on the first day and a mistrial was declared. During the second trial, the 'painful details' incidental to the medical testimony required another juror to be removed to the open air. While he was taking deep breaths of the London smog outside the building, back in the courtroom the judge admonished the Crown counsel 'that it was quite unnecessary to go into those matters with such minuteness, particularly as the jury probably would understand very little of such a subject' — advice which, if observed as a precedent, would have reduced the reports of many subsequent Victorian murder trials to mere pamphlet size.[1]

But the sensation of the trial was the fall from grace of the distinguished expert, Dr Alfred Swaine Taylor. Testifying before the magistrates immediately after Smethurst was arrested, he had described how he had analysed the contents of many bottles of supposed medicine found in Smethurst's possession. Only in Bottle 21 had he found

1. The bench's concern for the jury's limited powers of comprehension as well as its sensibilities was responsible for a number of moments of comedy in Victorian trials. In the trial of Mrs Maybrick the judge, admitting an exhibit in evidence, remarked, 'I don't know, gentlemen, that you would be very much edified by looking at this arsenic.' But medical ignorance was not confined to juries. In the same trial, his lordship 'asked for the meaning of the term "petechiae", with which he confessed himself unfamiliar.' Witness: 'It is the Italian [sic] for fleabite, my lord.' In the trial of Adelaide Bartlett a medical witness said, '. . . as far as I can remember, the lower part of the oesophagus was denuded of the epithelium.' The Attorney-General, taking no chances, turned to the bench: 'Your lordship does not need to have that explained to you, but perhaps it may be convenient to say that that long word means the gullet.' EDITOR'S NOTE: An account of the Maybrick case appears in an earlier volume of this series of anthologies, *The Lady Killers*, and the Bartlett case is recounted, by Richard D. Altick, in a still earlier volume, *The Christmas Murders*.

incriminating evidence, namely arsenic. He repeated this statement before the coroner's jury. Before the trial itself began, therefore, Smethurst's guilt was widely assumed on the basis of the arsenic in Bottle 21. But when Taylor came to the witness box in the Old Bailey, he had to confess a crucial mistake. In his analysis he had used the standard Reinsch's test, which involved boiling the substance in question in hydrochloric acid and then dipping a piece of copper foil or gauze into the solution. But Bottle 21 happened to have contained chlorate of potassium, which had the effect of liberating arsenic already contained, as an impurity, in the copper. He had therefore been betrayed by his own analysis: the arsenic to whose damning presence he swore came not from the property of the accused but from his own laboratory supplies. And no arsenic was found in the new Mrs Smethurst's organs.

This error provided one of the soundest bases for Smethurst's post-trial petition: the 'universal prejudice created in the public mind' by Taylor's deposition before the magistrates and the coroner's jury prevented a fair trial. There seems to have been much substance to the claim. A barrister who watched the proceedings wrote that 'Spectators, witnesses, prisoner's counsel, judge, jury, prosecuting counsel, one and all seemed weighed down, absolutely unable to escape from some mysterious weight hanging over their imaginations, which impelled them to a belief in the prisoner's guilt. Even the prisoner's counsel put his questions as though this evil influence led him every time to expect an unfavourable answer, and he got it.' The defence also failed to make adequate use of the considerable body of medical opinion it had on its side. This opinion held, in general, that Mrs Smethurst, who was proved to have been from five to seven weeks pregnant, died of gastric complications attendant to that condition. An obstetrician appearing for the defence cited the case of 'the celebrated Charlotte Brontë, who died of vomiting in pregnancy' — a convenient illustration he must have picked up in his non-professional reading, supposedly from Mrs

Gaskell's *Life of Charlotte Brontë*, which had appeared two years earlier.[1] Even the Crown prosecutor admitted in his opening statement that 'he was not prepared to say positively that death was due either to arsenic or antimony, but it was due to some poison or other, when and where administered he was unable to say'. The editor of the trial, himself a medical man, concludes that in his view 'the evidence, both circumstantial and scientific, completely failed to prove the guilt of Smethurst'.

But convicted he was, and at once both the medical and the legal professions raised an outcry. The *Dublin Medical Press* attacked Taylor in rhetorical periods customarily reserved for the nation's orators:

> The man who, *par excellence*, was looked upon as the pillar of medical jurisprudence; the man who it was believed could clear up the most obscure case, involving medico-legal considerations, ever brought into a Court of Justice; the man without whose assistance no criminal suspected of poisoning could be found guilty in England; the man whose opinion was quoted as the highest of all authorities at every trial where analysis is required, is the same who has now admitted the use of impure copper in an arsenic test where a life hung upon his evidence, the same who has brought an amount of disrepute upon his branch of the profession that years will not remove, the ultimate effects of which it is impossible to calculate, which none can regret with a deeper feeling of sorrow than ourselves, though, perhaps, in the end, a lesson may be taught which will not be lost upon the medical jurists, and which may tend to keep the fountain of justice clear and unpolluted.

1. A more remote link Smethurst had with literary history was occasioned by his having conducted, in 1847–52, a hydropathic establishment for 'people of the first station and character' at Moor Park, Surrey, formerly the home of Sir William Temple. Here Jonathan Swift, Temple's secretary for several years, wrote *A Tale of a Tub* and *The Battle of the Books*. While at Moor Park, Smethurst, for his part, edited *The Water Cure Journal*; but his most extensive literary effort was *Hydrotherapia; or, The Water-Cure, Together with a Short Sketch of the History of the Water-Cure from the Remotest Antiquity, and Remarks on Sea-Bathing* (1843).

When he regained his breath, the editorialist concluded: 'We must now look upon Professor Taylor as having ended his career, and hope he will immediately withdraw into the obscurity of private life, not forgetting to carry with him his favourite arsenical copper.' The valediction, though, was premature; notwithstanding this embarrassing episode, Taylor continued to be the high priest of British medical jurisprudence for eighteen more years.

Petitions, signed by many eminent lawyers and medical men, were handed in to the Home Secretary, Sir George Cornewall Lewis; three of the medical witnesses for the defence joined in a long, reasoned, particularised letter to the same official; the letter columns of *The Times* were filled with additional comment, most of it in Smethurst's favour. The Home Secretary compounded the furor by referring the case for adjudication to 'the best-known surgeon in London', Sir Benjamin Collins Brodie. After studying the transcript, Sir Benjamin reported that 'there is not absolute and complete evidence of Smethurst's guilt'. Lord Chief Justice Baron Pollock, who had presided at the trial and had been severely criticized for his biased summing-up, justly complained that this was 'a most unprecedented course' — Sir Benjamin, though competent to decide medical issues, had exceeded his authority by going into 'matters & motives — probabilities — purchase of *poison* ... in short ... he overrules the conclusion of the jury.'[1]

---

1. Wilkie Collins used this and the following detail of the Smethurst case in his long and undeservedly neglected suspense story, *Armadale*, serialized in the *Cornhill Magazine* in 1864–66. In the novel, after the conviction of a woman for poisoning her husband, there is a great outcry in the press: 'Doctors who had *not* attended the sick man, and who had *not* been present at the examination of the body, declared by dozens that he had died a natural death. Barristers without business, who had *not* heard the evidence, attacked the jury who had heard it, and judged the judge, who had sat on the bench before some of them were born.' As a result, the Home Secretary consults the judge, who refuses to take any action but consents to 'having the conflict of medical evidence submitted to one great doctor; and when the one great doctor took the merciful view, after expressly stating, in the first instance, that he knew nothing practically of the merits of the case, the Home Secretary was perfectly satisfied'. The convicted woman is pardoned. But to satisfy public feeling that she should be punished a little, she is then tried and convicted on a charge of robbery.

Smethurst (who had an advantage Palmer did not enjoy, in that his record was clean) was therefore granted a pardon. The law, however, insisting on an ounce of flesh if it was to be deprived of its pound, had him re-arrested and tried for bigamy. He was convicted and served a year at hard labour. At liberty once more, he had the effrontery to sue his late wife's next of kin, who were trying to prove her will void since, they maintained, it was signed under duress and the already-ailing testator was of unsound mind. Although this audacious move could not have been expected to create a favourable impression, nothing ventured, nothing gained. And Smethurst won his case!

If public confidence in expert testimony had been shaken by the doctors' disagreements in Palmer's case, it was shattered by the 'absolutely and uncompromisingly contradictory' evidence in Smethurst's. 'It is hardly to be wondered at,' remarks the trial editor, 'that a layman should have doubts as to the value of scientific testimony, if that were a sample.' And apart from the all-too-palpable contradictions, there was the question of the various doctors' professional credentials. Smethurst himself had his MD from Erlangen University, and although the record does not specify, as it does in the later case of Dr Pritchard, who was a fellow-alumnus of Erlangen, the likelihood is that he got it over the counter rather than earned it in the classroom and laboratory. Erlangen, like Giessen and Heidelberg, was noted for its sale of medical degrees on easy terms. Even so, an Erlangen MD was as impressive a credential as the 'Archbishop of Canterbury's degree' held by one witness.

> Q. What! Can he [the Archbishop] make a doctor of medicine?
> A. [By the judge] Yes; and he can also make a master of arts.
> Q. Did you take your degree as a matter of course?
> A. [By witness] Oh, dear, no! It is a very uncommon thing. I had to get a certificate from two members of the College of Physicians, stating that they had

> known me for a length of time, and that I was a
> proper person to have the degree.

The Archbishop of Canterbury's fitness to pass upon the
qualifications of a man proposing to undertake the cure of
bodies may have been marginal, but it was hallowed by
long usage, for the so-called Lambeth degrees had been
given legal standing by an act of 1533.

In 1858, a year before Smethurst came to trial, nearly two
dozen corporate bodies and officials had the power to grant
licences for medical practice. By an act of 1511, even before
the Archbishop of Canterbury received his diploma-
granting privilege, men wishing to practise medicine in
London, except for Oxford and Cambridge graduates, had
to be examined and approved by the Bishop of London or
the Dean of St Paul's, and in the country by the bishop of
the diocese – in every instance, with at least nominal
professional advice. By Smethurst's time, medical education and licensing in Britain had become utter chaos.
Alongside the fellows and licentiates of the London College
of Physicians and MDs from British universities – the
most prestigious if not necessarily the most knowledgeable
physicians – all kinds of other so-called medical men
assumed the title of 'doctor' or 'surgeon': apothecaries,
holders of diplomas from continental medical schools,
barbers, even chemists. No wonder, then, that there was a
strong movement to create one central agency to standard-
ise medical qualifications. This was accomplished by the
Medical Act of 1858, which created the General Medical
Council. But the law was not retroactive, so that a pre-1858
practitioner, however obscure his qualifications, could
minister as before. Mid-Victorian murder trials therefore
continued to feature, as 'expert' witnesses, medical men
who conceivably could not have passed the new standard
examinations.

The Smethurst case was not among the most 'popular'
Victorian murders, in the sense that it did not enthrall the

public as Palmer's had done. The excitement it generated was chiefly in educated circles; its sensationalism appealed to the intellect rather than to the rude fancy. But even here, the student of Victorian social life does not go unrewarded. For this was the time — the middle and late 1850s — when the evangelical passion for strict Sabbatarian observance, which kept the Lord's Day unconscionably dull and joyless throughout the Queen's reign, reached its peak. In the early summer of 1855, Lord Robert Grosvenor introduced into the House of Commons a bill which, 'to secure the better observance of the Lord's Day,' sought to add to the existing Sabbatarian restrictions a ban upon the Sunday operation of trains and steamboats and upon the opening of public places of refreshment. For several Sundays thereafter, Hyde Park was the scene of riotous protests directed initially against the aristocrats who followed their custom of taking Sunday afternoon drives through the park. These high-born Sabbath breakers were greeted with groans, hisses, and cries of 'Go to church!' On one such Sunday, 150,000 people were estimated to have gathered in the park, necessitating heavy police reinforcements (who were later charged, in respectable quarters, with over-reacting to the mob's unruliness) and sending over a hundred persons to the station house or the hospital. On another occasion crowds surged through nearby Belgravia, breaking the windows of mansions with paving blocks, Paris-style. The disaffection between classes was intensified by the knowledge that Lord Robert's bill specifically exempted Pall Mall clubs. In the end, the working-class protests, assisted by a substantial body of middle-class sympathisers, had their effect, and the provocative bill was withdrawn.

The most noteworthy literary documents reflecting the controversy are *Little Dorrit*, serialised in 1855–57, in which Dickens illustrates (and bitterly assails) the Sabbatarian obsession, and Trollope's *Barchester Towers* (1855), in which the Reverend Obadiah Slope's rabid Sabbatarianism wins him the influential partisanship of Mrs Proudie and the detestation of her husband's broad-minded clergy. But alongside these novels stands, in a humble auxiliary role, the record of the Smethurst trial. It is no accident, but rather a faithful representation of the current spirit, that no fewer than three separate allusions to Sunday observance occur in the case. The Richmond solicitor whom Smethurst asked to come to Isabella's sickbed and execute her will testified, 'I told him I did not like to do business on a Sunday, and that the law did not like wills being executed on a Sunday'. Swallowing his scruples, however, he did it just the same, and collected his fee before he left the house. Dr Taylor testified that he performed his analysis of specimens from Isabella, while she was still living, because 'I was told that it was necessary to do something to save the life of this lady, and therefore, contrary to my custom of not making analyses on a Sunday, I proceeded with my experiment'. It was as a result of this reluctant violation of the Sabbath that Smethurst was arrested the next day, but Isabella did not benefit by it; she died on the Tuesday. So pervasive were qualms about the desecration of the Day of Rest that, although Monday was traditionally the day appointed for executions in Surrey, where the alleged crime occurred, considerable opposition was expressed to the necessity of men working on the Sabbath to erect the scaffold atop Horsemonger Lane Gaol. The day therefore was altered to Tuesday, but thanks to Smethurst's reprieve, the gallows were not used.

And so the formidable presence of the English Sunday affected lawyers and doctors and all manner of men; it was sometimes a veritable matter of life and death, because it might have added a day to Smethurst's life had the crisis not been averted. Hangmen too must have a day reserved for their pious exercises. And murderers? I have not tried to count the Victorian homicides that were enacted on the Lord's Day, but my impression is that murderers as a class were not Sabbatarians. At least, when a man or woman was set upon accomplishing the fatal deed, the Biblical admonition to keep the Lord's Day holy proved no deterrent. There may be some kind of significance in the fact that several of the goriest transactions in Victorian annals did occur on Sunday. It is worth noticing that one of the Sabbath breakers, William Sheward of Norwich, required a whole week to dispose of his victim's remains, so that it was not until late on the seventh day following that he could rest.

Dentist in the Chair

❦❦

RICHARD WHITTINGTON-EGAN

ARTHUR WARREN WAITE was every other inch a charmer. Those 'other', non-charming inches? Pure, unadulterated psychopath.

The infant Arthur drew well in the chromosome lottery. A child of fortune. The good fairy at his crib-side handed out a generous package of gifts — fine physique, sharp intelligence, slender good looks, athletic prowess, charm of manner — but he was also touched, with fatal consequences, by the wand of the bad fairy, who bestowed upon him a single quality which was to destroy all the others: psychopathy.

Although, so it has been said, he was actually born in Canonsburg, a small township some twenty miles southwest of Pittsburgh, Pennsylvania, all accounts agree that he was reared in the bustling Michigan city of Grand Rapids.

His parents were by no means well-to-do, but they were good and dutiful folk, anxious that their boy should do well. He was encouraged in every possible way and provided with the very best education that they could afford. After he had attended the Grand Rapids grade and high schools, from which he graduated satisfactorily, his parents, at some sacrifice, sent him to the dental college at the University of Michigan, Ann Arbor, whence he emerged in due course a fully qualified dentist.

Having no expectation of an inheritance of any significant kind, his degree in dentistry his sole asset, Waite was faced with the prospect of earning a living in the profession for which he had been trained.

Now it so happened that at that time it was the beneficent custom of two Ann Arbor dental graduates of yesteryear, Messrs Wellman and Bridgeman, who had since done surpassingly well for themselves, having set up a veritable Dental Empire in South Africa, to cast a warm eye homewards and select their assistants from among the newly qualified, otherwise prospectless, alumni of their alma mater, and this was to provide Waite with his first chance in his new professional life. Since, however, under the British colonial law then obtaining in South Africa, no one was permitted to practise dentistry there without holding a certificate from a British university, Waite had first to go to Scotland. A bargain of some sort, perhaps not unconnected with an act of enlightened generosity on the part of the South African dental magnates, had been struck between Messrs Wellman and Bridgeman and the dental school at the University of Glasgow, whereby certificates would be granted to the laureated Michigan dentists applying for employment by Messrs Wellman and Bridgeman after only a few weeks of lecture-attendance and examination.

This not very strenuous post-graduate ordeal behind him, and in consequence thereof styling himself now a dental *surgeon*, Waite arrived in Capetown at the beginning of 1910, to embark upon his five-year-contract life as a journeyman dentist on the Wellman and Bridgeman circuit — their chain of dental offices throughout Cape Colony.

Starting off in one of the firm's Capetown offices, his subsequent extensive travels involved brief periods of drill-and-forceps duty in various towns, villages, kraals and mining settlements, before, in 1913, he was given charge of a branch office in Durban, Natal.

Then something went badly wrong. His contract with Messrs Wellman & Bridgeman was cut short. He had been filling, it would seem, not only clients' teeth, but also, and even more liberally, his own pockets, with dental gold.

There were tales of missing stocks tooth-marked for the inlays and bridges of Cape Colony. Within weeks of the outbreak of World War One, he sailed back to the United States, his baggage comfortingly lined with twenty thousand dubiously-acquired dollars.

The man in his late twenties returning from South Africa in the fall of 1914 was a completely different proposition from the callow, sallow, lanky lad who had left Grand Rapids half a decade before. Handsomely sun-tanned, tall, well-proportioned, athletic, clean-limbed, clear-eyed, clean-shaven, a successful dental surgeon, a crack tennis-player, perfectly groomed, unfailingly urbane, now speaking with a British accent and calling himself *Dr* Waite, he hit Grand Rapids like a superman from another planet.

Displaying all the sophistication and *savoir-faire* of the far-travelled get-up-and-go man, an adept practitioner of the wit-spangled conversation of the *homme du monde*, the cosmopolitan, who seems able to talk easily, entertainingly, informatively and authoritatively on practically any subject under the sun, he proved an irresistibly attractive companion to men and women alike; although, it has to be admitted, his superlative attraction was to women, and most especially to women older than himself. He exerted, effortlessly, the gigolo effect. He inspired faith and accepted trust. His broad, toothy smile never, but *never*, faded. He was always, through thick and thin, the smiler.

But Arthur Warren Waite was like one of those teeth which he must often have come across in the course of his 'open wide, please' days: perfect, bright, shining white, on the outside ... but inside — deep down, hidden — rotting with caries.

The dazzled natives looked and marvelled, but did not see. Small wonder that Grand Rapids, eye-balling only the toothsome man, the beamish odontologist, received this errant son with open, wide, pleased arms.

If Grand Rapids viewed Arthur Warren Waite with optimism, that gentleman assuredly returned the compliment. And in so doing he bethought himself of a young woman, by three years his junior, named Clara Louise Peck. The memory was practical rather than romantic. The two had known each other since they were children and had in fact attended school together before Clara had been hied off to the Chevy Chase School in Washington, preparatory to a period at Columbia University, Manhattan.

One must, I fear, interject at this point the unpalatable fact that the dazzlesome Arthur Warren Waite was a gentleman to whom money was dearer than all else in this universe; dearer, indeed, as was sadly to prove the case, than the deepest family ties. It was a divine article of his creed that you cannot pay too great a price for money, provided, of course, that others foot the bill. And not only was Waite a young man with an overweening love of the multi-coloured dollar, and a ruthless determination to acquire lots of them, but he was the original get-rich-quick guy — for, despite his name, the one thing that Arthur could not, would not, do was wait. He was a young man in a tearing hurry to, by hook or by crook, make himself a millionaire.

Clara Peck's position in the Arthur Waite scheme of things becomes clear when it is revealed that she was the only daughter of John E. Peck, millionaire drug manufacturer.

One has no wish to be ungallant, but, indisputably, Clara was not a beauty. Rather a heavy-featured girl — lips rather too thick, nose rather too fleshy, chin rather too solid. But beauty lies in the eye of the beholder, and in this case the beholder's eye was firmly fixed upon Miss Peck's beautiful inheritance. A Peck was not to be sniffed at as a marriage partner, for the dowry would be munificent and the legacy magnificent.

Waite, it must in fairness to him be allowed, worked hard at the wooing of Clara. Whatever his other faults, in dynamism he was not lacking — at least where self-promotional interests were involved. He got himself invited to a reception at the Peck mansion. He was assiduous in his attentions to his prospective heiress. He smiled . . . and

91

smiled ... and smiled. *So* nice and good natured! He
followed the Pecks to Florida for the winter 1914–15
holiday, and there, at Palm Beach, took part in a number
of tennis tournaments, bewitching the Pecks by the sheer,
ferocious brilliance of his performance on the court.

For all the shop-window lay-out of the young man's
sterling qualities, it was far from being a quick and easy
courtship. The Pecks, acutely aware of the perils of fortune-
hunters, harboured a bushel of suspicions. Gradually,
though, with skill and cunning, the indefatigable charmer
smiled and smoothed and smarmed his way into the
family's confidence.

They even began to like him. He didn't drink or smoke.
They never heard him swear. He seemed so genuinely
devoted to Clara. He was such a brilliant doctor. (Somehow he seems to have made them believe that he was not
just a dentist, but a medical man also, and not just a medical
man, but a highly-skilled surgeon. All of which speaks
volumes for the sagacity of poverty and the ignorance of
wealth.)

Clara and Arthur became officially engaged.

On Thursday, 9 September 1915, at Fountain Street
Baptist Church, in one of the grandest of Grand Rapids
weddings, the Reverend Alfred W. Wishart officiating,
Clara Louise Peck became Mrs Arthur Warren Waite.

Phase One of the Master Plan successfully completed.
Now he really had something to smile about.

The Waites' honeymoon was brief: just a few days in
Detroit, albeit at the de luxe Pontchartrain Hotel, overlooking the river.

It came as quite a surprise in a number of quarters that,
after his return from honeymoon, Waite did not open up
a practice in Grand Rapids. But no, he said, opportunities
for advancement in his profession were much greater in
New York, and it was to that city that 'Dr' and the new
Mrs Waite headed.

There, they found awaiting them – on Riverside Drive,

one of Manhattan's most glamorous addresses in those days, at No 435, on the 116th Street parallel – a sumptuous, seven-room apartment, which, rent-free and lavishly furnished, was old John Peck's present to them. He had also made his daughter an allowance of $300 a month. Far from being grateful, Waite was angrily disappointed. He regarded apartment and allowance as a pittance, measured against the high-stacked columns of the old man's money. He had calculated on an outright gift of $50,000 – cash.

A couple of months before the wedding, Waite had enrolled at New York's Cornell Medical School, paying on registration an advance fee of $225 which he, having presumably blown the twenty-thousand dollar gold-tooth haul on rich living in the year since his return from South Africa, had only managed to raise by cashing-in a small insurance policy which had somehow survived the spend-spend-spend spree. Now, securely married to money, the impulse to serious, disciplined medical study had evaporated, and, informing the school that he was leaving the city, he obtained a refund of $200.

'Dr' Waite did not immediately engage offices in which to pursue private practice in New York. He was, he explained, very fully stretched as a staff consultant in surgery – dental and otherwise – at several hospitals.

He had other fish to fry, too.

The personable young 'doctor' had made instant impact on the circles of Upper West Side society to which his new wife had introduced him, and was much in demand among the lion-cub-hunting hostesses of New York.

His *chutzpa* with a tennis-racket served as an added attraction. When, after winning a number of tournaments, he became Metropolitan Indoor Tennis Champion, his stock rose to dizzy heights; the fashionable columnist, Franklin P. Adams, and other celebrated tennis-addicts, hailed him as 'the best player on the local courts', and his wife swelled with pride. 'He's Metropolitan Amateur Champion,' she wrote triumphantly to her parents. 'Isn't that wonderful?'

To all appearances, Arthur Warren Waite was now a well

set-up, fortunate young man, blessed with a devoted wife and a millionaire father-in-law. His mother-in-law adored him. In her bedazzled eyes, her precious son-in-law could do no wrong. She regarded him as a brilliant and dignified addition to the family, and was prepared to stump up all the financial support that might be necessary to put Arthur in a position to carry out any research work which he thought would help him to advance in his great calling. It was like being presented with a blank cheque. And Mr Peck's spinster sister, Clara's Aunt Catherine, who, by the by, had given each of the couple $3000 as a wedding present, had also fallen completely under the spell of the medicinal enchanter. So completely did she trust, and so highly did she value his advice, that on one of his many fond and dutiful little visits to her at the Park Avenue Hotel, where, lapped in comfortable elegance, she lived, she was easily persuaded to let him bear away $40,000 to invest for her. On some subsequent visit she unhesitatingly handed over a power of attorney which gave him access to most of her liquid assets.

It was on this money that Waite was living, pretending that the wherewithal to maintain Clara and his grand style of living came as the harvest of his quite exceptional medico-dental skills.

Clara, it must be clearly understood, firmly believed that her husband was in practice as a doctor. Had he not taken her on several occasions to the Flower Hospital, asked her to remain briefly in the waiting room, and returned, full of apologies, an hour or so later, announcing with a modest smile that he had just completed a vital, life-saving emergency operation ...?

Proud as she was of him, and of the fact that New York's most prestigous hospitals had recognized and appreciated his talents, Clara could not help feeling a mite lonely. Arthur seemed to have so little time for her. Of course, she told herself (and others), he's busy: he has his profession and his tennis; I mustn't be selfish. She was more than understanding about his long and frequent absences. He had to be out many evenings visiting his patients. Quite a few night calls, too. Sometimes he was so hard-pressed that he did not return until the early hours of the morning. Sometimes she thought he was *too* good – that he was sacrificing too much of his life for others.

Had poor Clara known what her husband was really up to during those long stretches away from Riverside Drive, she would have been a *mariée* far less complacent. The reprehensible truth is that when he was not, for sinister reasons, tinkering with his test-tubes and petri dishes of plague and pestilence, his agar plates and bouillon bowls of cultivated pathogens, he was tinkering with a younger woman named Horton. *Mrs* Horton.

The bold Arthur had first encountered the beautiful Mrs Horton when, far from the life-and-death drama and the brave blaze of the operating-theatre arcs, he had been prosaically taking a voice-culture course at the YMCA and learning French and German the Method Way with the Berlitz.[1]

Margaret Weaver Horton, the twenty-years-younger wife of forty-one-year-old Henry Mack Horton, variously described as distinguished aeronautical engineer, broker, and dealer in war supplies, of 56 West Eleventh Street, was, after some small success as an actress and chanteuse, ambitious to become an opera singer (disquieting echoes here of Kunigunde Mackamotzki, *vulgo*: Belle Elmore, who tied the knot with, and the rope for, little Dr Crippen). Bowled over by the raven-haired Mrs Horton, Waite was to install her at the élite Hotel Plaza, facing the southern end of Central Park. An exceedingly plushy trysting place. Of this, as they say, more anon. Arthur Warren Waite was not so much bad seed as, to coin a diagnostic phrase, 'psycho seed'. Like all self-respecting psychopaths, he was

1. A variant version has Waite seeing her performing at the Strand Theatre in December 1915, and at the Academy of Music the following January. Smitten, he had managed to get himself introduced to her; then, turning on all the old wistful Waite smiling charm, induced her to join him in French and German lessons at the Berlitz School, hinting that there might well be a sequel of extensive foreign travel.

subject to the old world-owes-me-a-living syndrome. He has been described, and very perspicaciously, as 'the man who would be happy'. So he would — like any psychopath — at any cost — to anyone else. He presents a remarkable case of a totally amoral man. A cause unsuitable for treatment. He had decided to play family fortunes, which meant that he had to knock out his in-laws. So be it. The stakes were high.

Aunt Catherine had been unwise enough to play a gentle game of her own. The Will Game. Indiscreetly, she had discreetly let it be known that upon her demise — at some far distant date, of course — her favourite nephew-in-law would find himself in receipt of a very substantial *aide-mémoire* of his departed aunt.

Within the family, it was common knowledge that Mr Peck's will left half his fortune to his daughter.

So ... if Mr and Mrs Peck died, and Aunt Catherine died, and, perhaps, later on, Clara died, that would leave Arthur Warren Waite, a very rich and very eligible widower, the winner.

This had now become a matter for the ways-and-means committee in his divided skull. And this was where he could at last draw the interest on his long-time investment in a slightly more than dilettantish dedication to the healing art of the bacteriologist.

What can heal can also destroy.

Almost within hours of his arrival with his still-blushing bride in New York, Waite had started to mount his carefully planned and homicidally orientated assault upon the metropolitan citadel of orthodox medicine. Practising one of those small deceptions which came so easily to him, he let it be generally understood — and, indeed, it came to be widely believed — that he was a fully-qualified medical doctor.

He further fostered the belief, seemingly ratified by the exclusivity and rich appointments of his Riverside Drive apartment, that he was a man of wealth, taste and culture, and that he was benevolently interested in scientific research — particularly in the study of the microbic causes of disease.

For fell purposes of his own, as we shall presently come to recognise, he proceeded to cultivate those who would be able to provide him with an entrée to the somewhat arcane world of bacteriology.

On 17 September 1915 — eight days after his wedding — Waite began his close-focus scrutiny of the microscopic death-dealers, working under the guidance of Dr Louis Heitzman at his laboratory on 78th Street.

The following month, a bacteriological practitioner named Moos was invited to the apartment on Riverside Drive, where Waite had fixed up a small laboratory, and was anxious to discuss with this expert the comparative efficacies of the various techniques for growing cultures of bacteria. He was, Waite volunteered, engaged in research at Fordham Hospital, and had been supplied with cultures of diphtheria and typhoid bacilli.

'Dr' Waite had also succeeded in getting himself introduced to Dr Percival de Nyce, associate pathologist and skilled bacteriologist and virologist at New York's highly-respected Flower Hospital. Dr Nyce was impressed by Waite's obvious keenness and dedication, but could not help noticing that it was only in the most deadly germs and viruses that he appeared to be really interested, and was slightly puzzled when he complained that the bacteria with which he was currently engaged were not sufficiently virulent for the experiment he had in mind.

It is time now to drop any pretence that Waite's interest was humanitarian, that he cherished a dream of becoming another Pasteur or Koch, saviour of suffering mankind. The experiment he had in mind, had had in mind from the start, was the killing of his in-laws.

With quite extraordinary alacrity — within weeks of their moving into No 435 — Clara's young husband had issued an affectionate invitation to 'Dad' and 'Mother', as he called his Peck-in-laws, to pay the still billing and cooing newly-weds a visit at their golden nest, to stay with them for a while.

Flattered — and touched — that 'the children' wanted them, Mr and Mrs Peck were delighted to accept. They did not, however, remain for very long on that first visit. The air of New York did not seem to agree with Mr Peck. From practically the moment he arrived, he began to feel off-colour, run down, very different from his usual bouncy self.

Arthur, sympathy personified, diagnosed a coming cold, made up a special medicine for him, and even took the solicitous trouble to spray his father-in-law's throat each evening. All to no avail. Still feeling very seedy, Mr Peck dolefully returned to Grand Rapids and the therapeutic bosom of his own physician, who, after thoroughly over-hauling him and finding nothing wrong, expressed total puzzlement. Once back home, however, the indisposition, whatever it was, soon passed, and the old drugs magnate was rapidly humming away as healthily and cost-effectively as ever.

That had been, as it were, the dummy run. That was that for the present.

If at first you don't succeed. . . .

Wreathed in smiles, the good 'Dr' Waite turned his thoughts to a profitable future.

Now Arthur Warren Waite's dream scenario unfolds.

It was Christmas . . . season of goodwill . . . ice on the ornamental waters of Central Park . . . and in the cold heart of 'Dr' Waite. It was in no spirit of Dickensian cordiality that he invited the old couple from the Middle West to come and spend a jolly Yuletide in New York. His motive was very ulterior.

Unfortunately, or perhaps not, Mr Peck had to remain for business reasons in Grand Rapids: so, instead, the Waites joined Dad and Mother at the Peck mansion.

Arthur, however, was not able to stay for more than a few festive days. Oh, so regretfully, he had to return to New York to perform a delicate eye operation.

Clara remained behind. On 10 January 1916, she returned home, bringing her mother with her.

Mrs Peck was permitted but a short spell of enjoyment of the excitements of the big city before being suddenly stricken by a mysterious illness which taxed even the diagnostic genius of her brilliant son-in-law.

A local physician, Dr William H. Porter, was called in. His diagnostic ability proved no better than that of the unqualified Waite. Kidney disease, he decided at length, and prescribed accordingly. He took an optimistic view, saying that in his opinion there was no real cause for anxiety.

'Dr' Waite most strongly disagreed. Endowed with that strange instinct with which the merest handful of truly outstanding doctors seem to be gifted, he felt the gloomiest forebodings. Mother was, he pronounced with great distress, very seriously ill.

How sadly right he was. How markedly, as he predicted, she failed to respond to treatment.

Clara would afterwards gratefully recall the exemplary way in which Arthur had tended her ailing mother. He brought her flowers and foot-warmers, and, for all the pressures of his demanding professional life, found time to spend long hours playing her favourite gramophone records and crooning to her at her bedside.

Later, Clara would remember, too, the strange incident of the gas in the night. It occurred about a week before her mother's death. Arthur was out at the time, ostensibly visiting his patients, and Clara had, as was so often her custom nowadays, gone off alone and lonely to her bed. She had not retired long, was just drifting, relaxed, into a hypnagogic state, when suddenly she was wide awake, a strong smell of gas in her nostrils. She promptly got up, investigated, and found that the smell was coming from her mother's room. The tap of the unlit gas-fire had been left turned on. Had it not been that one of the windows was inconspicuously partly open – for she noticed, too, that by some malevolent mischance a rug had somehow positioned itself suffocatingly against the bedroom door – her mother would undoubtedly have been asphyxiated.

Arthur and Clara took it in turns to nurse Mrs Peck. He

chose particularly to watch over the patient at night. That was typical of him. Kind and thoughtful as ever, he obviously wanted his wife to get her proper quota of sleep. But, despite all the loving care and attention lavished upon her by the 'children', the patient, fulfilling 'Dr' Waite's prophecy, continued to deteriorate. Poor Mrs Peck passed away in the small hours of Sunday, 30 January.

Dr Porter, who had opined that there was 'no real cause for anxiety', perhaps slightly shamefacedly, but at any rate readily enough, gave his certification of death as the result of kidney disease.

Mrs Peck had been precisely twenty days in the dying.

The lamentations of none were louder than those of the grief-stricken son-in-law. Herculean, he pulled himself together. A great comfort to his grieving wife, he sorted out certificates and permits and attended to all the irksome formality requirements for the return of the septuagenarian Mrs Peck's body to Grand Rapids. He hustled and bustled and rounded up Clara and Aunt Catherine, efficiently conveyed them to the station, and got them safely aboard the train to Michigan.

And, on arrival there, he busied himself further, making all the arrangements for the cremation.

Cremation? Oh, yes, didn't they know...? Hadn't he told them? To be cremated, that was Mother's last wish, whispered to him just before she died.

Among the eyebrows that shot up were those of the Reverend Wishart, that same pastoral gentleman who, it will be remembered, had performed, only a few months before, the joyous ceremony of Arthur and Clara's wedding, and must now conduct the burial service of the bride's mother. He could not help thinking it odd that Mrs Peck should have decided to be cremated, *to have thus inexplicably changed her mind,* for she had specifically told him — and not all that long ago — that she wanted to be buried in the family vault.

Her widower, seventy-two years old, numbed by the shock of sudden bereavement, couldn't remember what his wife had ever said about burial or cremation, but was happy to accept the caring Arthur's word as to Mother's wishes.

In a sort of compromise, her ashes were buried in the Peck family vault.

Waite felt well pleased with himself. Not only had he seen to it that Mrs Peck's dying wish was honoured, but he had also ensured that all chance — or mischance — of anyone's discovering the true cause of the old lady's decease had been licked away by the red flames, gone up in the grey smoke, of the crematorium.

Two days after 'Mother's' death, the loving son-in-law sat down and wrote a letter to Archibald B. Morrison, the Peck family attorney. In it he asked: 'What will become of Mr Peck's money now that Mrs Peck is dead? Will Mr Peck make a new will?' Then added, sowing seeds: 'He is old and in poor health.' That was wishful, rather than truthful, thinking. It was, in point of fact, flatly contradicted by a statement in a letter which, not long before he died, John Peck wrote to a druggist friend of his: 'I am quite well, and not only that, I am taking good care of my physical body.'

That letter was written in February from New York, whither, a week or two after his wife's cremation, he had gone. The great house in Grand Rapids had grown lonely, and old John, overwhelmed by the loss of his lifelong companion, finding the empty, echoing rooms of his grand mansion the demesne of memories unbearable, had been really glad to take advantage of his fond son-in-law's warm invitation. He and his daughter had dearly loved Mrs Peck, and it was only natural that they should be eager to be together in this sad season, to console each other in their shared sorrow.

How should he know that things had been so ordered that he had come east to go west?

All blissfully unaware, how pleasant it was to sit back in an easy-chair beside the wide, commanding window in the apartment on Riverside Drive, basking in the warmth and radiance of the children's love, watching the sun 'going down in crimson suds' over the Hudson, and then as 'came still evening on, and twilight gray', and the first yellow pinheads of night-lights pierced and rocked and shimmered on the dark river's water, to look forward to all the earthy delights of his favourite dishes religiously served to him at dinner.

There is no doubt that old John E. Peck loved his victuals. That, indeed, was the trouble — according to Dr A. A. Moore, the medical man summoned when, a matter of days after the beginning of his visit, Mr Peck fell ill. Nasty digestive disturbance, said the doctor, scribbling a palliative prescription — something soothing for diarrhoea. Nothing to worry about.

Again, as in the case of Mrs Peck, 'Dr' Waite disagreed. With solemn shake of head, he declared: 'He hasn't a very strong constitution. I shouldn't be surprised if he did not live for long.' And again, Waite's prophecy was to prove superior to Dr Moore's diagnosis. But then, as will presently appear, in this case, as previously, Waite's accuracy resulted from a bit of insider trading.

During the days that followed, Mr Peck's son-in-law was most attentive. The sick man did not like his medicine. 'Dr' Waite found a way round that little difficulty. One evening he came into the kitchen and, quite openly, poured some of the medicine into Dad's soup. He came into the kitchen again later, when a pot of tea was being prepared for Dad, and poured more medicine into the tea-pot.

'Mr Peck didn't like his soup, Dora,' he told their coloured servant, 'so I must put some more medicine in his tea.'

Dr Moore's first visit had been on 5 March. He paid further visits throughout the next week. On the occasion of one of those, Waite drove Dr Moore to his next domiciliary and, en route, asked him: 'If Mr Peck doesn't get well, do you think you ought to tell Clara?' To which Moore replied: 'Well, Dr Waite, don't let's be so pessimistic. I think Mr Peck will be all right.'

Mr Peck, like Mrs Peck, died on a Sunday — 12 March 1916 — six weeks to the day after his wife. That morning, when Dr Moore called, he was met at the door by Waite. 'I'm afraid something has happened to Mr Peck,' he said. 'It seems to me he has died.'

That was one diagnosis in which they concurred.

Once more, there was no suspicion of wrongdoing. No difficulty about the issuing of a death certificate. 'Acute indigestion complicated by heart failure' was the given cause.

Clara Waite had become a rich orphan.

Events clicked into a familiar pattern. It was like the replay of an old B-movie. Clockwork precision. Clockwork efficiency. Arthur again taking over all the arrangements — registrars, undertakers, embalmers, transportation. Arthur again escorting Clara and Aunt Catherine to the station, seating them safely in the five o'clock Grand Rapids train.

Beside them, Arthur sank back with well-earned satisfaction into the comfortable first-class cushioning.

Before them, riding westward in the baggage-car ahead, Mr Peck, in his coffin, heading towards the all-consuming, all-truth-hiding flames of the crematorium.

And it was still only Monday, 13 March.

The little family party — and the corpse — arrived. Waiting on the platform at Grand Rapids station to meet them were Clara's only, and older, brother, Percy, the Peck family physician, Dr Perry Schurtz, and the ubiquitous Reverend Wishart.

Encore, Waite wept dutifully upon the shoulders of the various members of the Peck pack, delivered up a mournful threnody on the passing of a great, and greatly loved, man, and quietly, diffidently almost, announced his father-in-law's last pathetic wish: that he, like his wife, should be cremated, and his ashes mingled with hers.

Then the clockwork spring broke.

This time there was to be no easy acquiescence, no obedient bending of the family will to the alleged burning desire of the dear departed.

'Everything's fixed,' said Waite in businesslike tones. 'I've arranged for poor Dad's body to go right on to

Detroit to be cremated. I'll go with it and see this sad business finished. Would any of you folks like to come with me?'

Percy, prickly, exuding hostility, turned on him. 'Just a minute,' he said. 'I guess we aren't in all that hurry to see the last of Father. I'll see to the coffin.'

Lip-line tightening, face paling, Waite listened in astonishment. He could hardly believe what he was hearing. The *ingratitude* of it. But he was careful enough, clever enough, not to raise any objections, not to argue.

Percival Peck was demanding the baggage checks for the casket. Standing there, hand outstretched for them. A very slight but very awkward pause, during which everything seemed to be stock-still, suspended. Then, as though released from petrification by an enchanter's rod, wordlessly Waite handed them over. Percy ordered his father's body to be taken to the Grand Rapids undertakers, Sprattler's.

Later, a worried Waite called at Sprattler's. He asked to see the body, said he wanted to put a rose in the casket. His request was refused. He was denied admission.

What had gone wrong?

Of course, he knew nothing about the telegram ....

The telegram in question had arrived from New York shortly before Waite and his party. Addressed to Percival Peck, its message had been brief, disquieting and to the point.

> SUSPICIONS AROUSED. DEMAND AUTOPSY.
> KEEP TELEGRAM SECRET.
> K. ADAMS.

Neither Percy nor anyone else had the faintest idea who 'K. Adams' might be, but Percival Peck was not the sort of man to be deterred by a trifle like that. Besides, he had never liked Arthur, never been friendly with him. The others might gush and goo over him, fall for his charm, be taken in by that perpetual crocodile smile of his. Let them.

Prodded by the telegram, Percy had begun to see certain events in a new light — Arthur's urging the cremation of his mother, the suddenness of both his parents' deaths, how little he really knew about his brother-in-law. In the sudden perplexity of his situation, Percy decided to consult with the two men of the greatest probity that he knew — his family doctor and his pastor. They confirmed him in his instinct to take seriously, and act upon, the mysterious telegram.

Dr Schurtz admitted that he had never been entirely satisfied about Mrs Peck's death. He didn't know her wishes about being cremated, but he *did* know about her kidneys. They were, he could testify, as sound as a ten-year-old's when she left for New York. He had wondered wryly whatever she could have been drinking in that eastern metropolis?

Reverend Wishart, who had preached the funeral service over Mr Peck, after Percy had countermanded the onward transmission of the body to Detroit, said that he had noticed Waite, sitting nearby, 'staring weirdly' all through the service at the face in the open casket. After watching Waite's reactions throughout, Reverend Wishart found himself convinced by the close of the service that Waite was responsible for the death of the aged man. Call it Divine Inspiration — Reverend Wishart certainly would — or what you like, but it was 'that certain feeling' which beset Reverend Wishart and made him positive that Waite did it.

In order to discover the genesis of that all-important telegram, it is necessary to go back to the Sunday when John Peck died. That morning, Dr Jacob Cornell, of Somerville, New Jersey, a Peck relative who had several times brought other members of the family over the Hudson to visit 'Uncle John' during his sojourn at Riverside Drive, and knew that the old man had been latterly ailing and complaining, had received the news that he was dead.

Dr Cornell, taking his nephew, Arthur Swinton, with him, had gone at once to No 435. These inopportune callers were met at the door by Waite, who was up to his shifty eyes in the making of arrangements for the disposal of the body — embalmment and shipment to Detroit via Grand Rapids.

'What did you come for?' Waite asked rudely. 'I thought my wife had called you up and asked you not to come,' he added coldly, speaking through the half-open front-door.

Dr Cornell, gentlemanly, embarrassed, murmured something about feeling, under the circumstances, that it was his duty to call. Sullenly, grudgingly, Waite let the visitors, who had come to pay their last respects, in. They both noticed that he seemed nervous and distrait, that he had lost his usual urbanity and cordiality. Not only did he comport himself oddly before the visitors, but he would not permit them to view the body.

The mask of the smiler had slipped.

It was this inexplicable conduct towards his callers, in conjunction with the unwonted celerity Waite was displaying in getting his dead father-in-law's body embalmed and shipped off to Michigan, that set certain thumbs pricking. Dr Cornell refused to see anything sinister in Waite's behaviour; he, a nice-minded, charitable man, thought that it was either that Waite was just dreadfully upset by the death, or that there was some perfectly sound, but private, reason for the way he had gone on. Not so his sister, Elizabeth Hardwicke, listening that evening to the doctor's account of his ill-starred visit of condolence.

Mrs Hardwicke was frankly suspicious. She was one of those who thought that the haste with which the old man was being packed off back to Michigan, almost before he was cold, was, to say the very least of it, indecent. What was more, *she'd* never heard Uncle John complain of his heart or remark that there was anything wrong with it.

There was something else, and this was what had really set her antennae humming. On 22 February, just about the time that Mr Peck was taken seriously ill, she had happened to be having dinner at the Hotel Plaza with her daughter, Elizabeth, and Arthur Swinton, when 'Dr' Waite, in company with a striking raven-haired woman, had come into the restaurant. He had spotted her even as she spotted him. He promptly strode over to Mrs Hardwicke's table and, greeting her with, of course, a charming smile and easy confidence, told her that he had just completed an important operation at Bellevue Hospital. Then glibly added, with the bred-in-the-bone psychopath's snake-fast, forked tongue: 'I have brought my own special nurse here with me for dinner as I felt that she deserved something out of the ordinary for her skill and devotion to my work.' He said that after the meal they were to go on to another hospital, where he was to do another operation.

But Mrs Hardwicke was a shrewd and hard-nosed lady. She had watched Waite and his female companion and, putting one and one together, was perfectly certain that theirs was a deeper relationship than that of doctor and nurse. She had held her whisht, though — until, learning of Mr Peck's death in such quick succession to that of Mrs Peck, impelled by the strength of an almost psychic force, and in defiance of her brother's strict edict against interference, she had caused the mysterious telegram to be sent. One says 'caused' advisedly, because it was not she, but her daughter Elizabeth, who did the actual sending, for the very sensible reason that Mrs Hardwicke could not be *sure* that Arthur Warren Waite had worked lethal mischief on old Uncle John Peck, and if it all ended up in court with suings for libel, Elizabeth, a schoolteacher, not yet twenty-one and with no money or property of her own to speak of, could not be dunned for much in the way of damages.

Clara, who had become ill following the double shock of the loss, within six weeks and a day, of both her mother and father, decided to stay behind to recuperate in Grand Rapids. Her husband, thwarted of the cremation but with no clue of the edifice of suspicion which was now building against him, fully satisfied that he had successfully bluffed everyone, hurried back to his mythical medical responsibilities: in reality to the wine, women and song gaieties of the juicy Big Apple.

While, in all innocence (although that is hardly the right word to describe the good doctor's activities), Waite went about his affairs (now *that* is a much better word), things which would have caused him considerable unease were afoot in Grand Rapids.

After Reverend Wishart had concluded the funeral service, Mr Peck's body was not sent to the crematorium. Careful to drop no hint to Arthur of what was going on, Percy asked Dr Schurtz to arrange an autopsy. Its result showed that there had been no trace of mortal disease, and absolutely nothing wrong with the old man's heart. What the post-mortem did reveal were a number of suspicious gastro-intestinal lesions — in view of which, Dr Schurtz sent the viscera to Professor Victor Vaughan, Dean of the Medical School at the University of Michigan, for analysis.

A Reinsch test rapidly established the presence of arsenic. Since a man's life, as well as the determination of the mode of a man's death, depended upon its probative accuracy, the much lengthier and more complicated Marsh test was then set up in triplicate, to determine whether or not sufficient arsenic had been absorbed to cause death.

Actually, before Arthur had started back for New York, Percy and Dr Schurtz and Reverend Wishart, the self-appointed avenging trinity, had held a council of war and, as a first move in their campaign, hired a New York private eye, Raymond Schindler.

While the Waites were out of town, Schindler had finagled his way into their apartment and discovered a small wall-safe. In it were bank-books and a key. The latter proved to be that of a bank lock-box. Opened, it was found to be crammed full of dollars. They were the residue of the $40,000 entrusted to Waite by blandishment-blinded Aunt Catherine Peck for investment. Waite had sent $10,000 of this to his brother, Frank, with a note: 'There's more where this came from.'

From the second Waite stepped off the train in New York, he was shadowed, and Schindler, nipping smartly into an adjoining telephone booth at the station, overheard a call he made to Mrs Horton. He was telling her to check out of the Hotel Plaza at once.

The forces of private eye Schindler and his operatives were presently augmented by the detectional presence of Reverend Wishart. Convinced that the real truth about the terrible thing which had befallen the late member of his flock was to be learnt only among the sinful purlieus of the wicked city, the Peck family pastor, transformed into a Chestertonian figure – a kind of Baptist Father Brown – felt it his pastoral duty to travel east for a few whirlwind weeks of sleuthing in and about the aforesaid wicked city.

He came to New York in what he called a 'disguise' – a touchingly naive concept of such – clad still in his clerical blacks and greys, but with a light-grey fedora, worn 'at a jaunty angle'.

It was a role which nonetheless pricked the Reverend's conscience. He was later to deliver himself of such breast-beating *mea culpae* as: 'May the Lord forgive me for the lies and deceit that I practised ... I have done more lying since I have been here [in New York] than in all the rest of my life. I have lied and deceived, and, I expect, I have broken your laws. The Lord forgive me. I did it for what I believed to be the right. I have gone down on my knees and prayed for forgiveness for those sins.'

Whatever, between them – that is, Schindler and his operatives and Wishart and his divine inspiration – their multiple investigations had soon amassed a sufficiency of damning facts to alert and engage the professional curiosity of Assistant District Attorney Francis X. Mausco. And he, in turn, brought more investigators to dig yet deeper.

By now, with investigators amateur, private and public, zeroing in on him, Waite and his movements were as closely under the microscope as those of one of his beloved bacilli. A fourth, and very formidable, investigative group – hordes of newspaper reporters – was about to join the others, and all four would henceforth be united in the common effort to uncover and piece together the unwholesome *disjecta membra* of Arthur Warren Waite's shady life.

There followed a week of Startling Disclosures.

The newspapers, those valiant crusaders, those staunch watch-dogs of public interest, tireless searchers after the evil that men do, were busy conducting a thorough raking into Waite's mucky past. They were despatching their minions to quarter the city for news about him; their reporters were hounding him in his every, and even most innocent, movement. The stringers and legmen scoured not only New York and Michigan, but Glasgow and South Africa also, to bring in titbits for the winnowing. Some highly prejudicial Waite home-truths emerged.

For several days the rumour that the suave young doctor had been in love with an exceptionally pretty woman frequently seen at the Hotel Plaza, where she had a studio, had been going the rounds. On the morning of 25 March, the New York dailies came out with full, circumstantial accounts of Waite's philanderings. The 'debonair doctor', who had early discovered himself to be a man with power over women, had been by no means loth to exercise that peculiar influence. In silken dalliance he had distributed his favours both widely and generously, no lavish expense spared. But there was one lady who had eclipsed all others. They named a name. And published a picture. Of Mrs Margaret Horton.

Mrs Elizabeth Hardwicke recognised the young woman in the photograph.

Arthur and Margaret had registered at the Hotel Plaza as Dr and Mrs A.W. Walters (a wily matching of initials with those already marked upon his possessions) of New Rochelle, Westchester County.

Married less than six months, the doctor has been carrying on a passionate affair with a married singer – that was how the tabloids lip-smackingly tastefully put it.

Later, Mrs Horton, affecting surprise at the conclusions dirty-minded folk drew from the simple desire of two people to be alone to test their language skills without the embarrassment of strangers hearing their slips, protested: 'We were never there at night. There was no bed in the room. It was fitted up as any artistic studio in a hotel would be. It was just a room to study and practise between classes.'

Although it was revealed that Waite had given Margaret Horton jewellery — valuable items which had been entrusted to him by Aunt Catherine Peck — she continued to insist that they had merely shared a common interest in art, music and foreign languages.

Mrs Horton's husband was at first very angry when he found out about the association between his wife and 'Dr' Waite, but, calming down, he said that he considered the relationship an innocent one. Margaret had, he said, made the kind of mistake of which any young woman might be guilty. That she had absolutely nothing to do with the crimes imputed to Waite, he was certain, and he was quite ready to forgive her.

Delving back into the dubious dentist's earlier life imported bad auspices. Tidings of peccadilloes past, a career of theft and petty crime, did not augur well for Waite's present credibility or future destiny.

As a boy, he had been in trouble on a number of occasions over thefts from his parents, relatives, schoolmates, employers and others.

At Dental College at Ann Arbor, he had been temporarily expelled from his fraternity for an act of dishonesty.

The temptation to steal money whenever the opportunity presented was one he could simply never resist. That he had never been arrested, let alone jailed, was solely due to the fact that he had always been shielded by his parents and always been in a position to make restitution.

At Glasgow University, there had been some chicanery. He had either used false papers to help him to get a quick degree, or imposed on the university authorities by some other form of misrepresentation.

In South Africa, he had tried to marry a young heiress of American parentage, but had been foiled when reports of his unsavoury reputation reached the ears of the girl's father.

'If at first you don't succeed . . .' Waite *had* tried again, in Grand Rapids, and had succeeded!

It was very soon after his rebuff by the heiress's father that Waite's contract with Messrs Wellman & Bridgeman was cut short. Suspected reason for requested resignation: those old light fingers. No way, the papers pointed out, could Waite have honestly saved $20,000 out of the sort of salary that he was being paid.

Revelations were coming in thick and fast, too, from those other — amateur, private, official — branches of the multiple investigation. From all sides the forces of retribution were converging upon Waite.

It was discovered that he had never taken the State Board examination to practise dentistry in New York; that he was not known at any of the hospitals to which he had claimed to be a consultant in surgery; that he had obtained from William Weber, an attendant at the Cornell Medical School, cultures of typhoid, diphtheria and pneumonia germs, and influenza virus.

Waite had, for a long while, been spending too freely. Under his father-in-law's will, the depleted coffers would, through Clara, have been refurbished. 'Dad' had left more than a million dollars — including a bequest of $2000 to Waite's father 'out of regard for his son'. He would have had no cause to worry about money for quite a time to come. And when, eventually, he had, there was still Aunt Catherine's legacy, and ... well, that could be arranged.

Now, in this blaze of bad publicity, this trial by the media, Waite knew that he had lost the devious game he had been so callously playing — just how unbelievably callously will in due course become clear. And it was now that he did something extremely peculiar. He telephoned Aunt Catherine and, in a voice crackling with strain and tension, asked her, 'What is the best thing for a man to do who has been cornered? Do you think suicide would be the right thing?'

A thoroughly flustered Aunt Catherine counselled most strongly against it.

It was at this precise psychological moment that the news broke that, after several days of tests, the toxicology laboratory at the University of Michigan had reported the discovery of arsenic somewhat in excess of five grains in Mr Peck's remains, and Waite decided to ignore Aunt Catherine's advice.

The police, coming somehow to hear of Waite's *felo de se* intent, arrived at Riverside Drive in time to scotch it. They found him, in the room adjoining that in which Mr and Mrs Peck had died, suffering from the effects of an overdose of the sleeping drug, sulphonal. He was still alive. The Master Venenator had failed to turn proficiently his veneficious art upon himself. Rushed to Bellevue Hospital, he was restored and revivified — in preparation for a ritual death to come.

Removed then to the detention ward at Bellevue, he was surrounded there by those who, in police pay, watched and listened. They caught him sending a draft for $1000 to his servant, Dora. He was trying to buy her false testimony. He wanted her to deny ever having seen him slip 'medicine' into his father-in-law's food and drink.

Waite was arrested for murder. He had a smile for the police. He also had a laugh at them. 'Why, the thing is too absurdly amusing even to discuss,' he chortled. District Attorney Edward H. Swann sat by his hospital cot-side. He had taken personal charge of the official investigation.

At first Waite denied everything.

He was coldly informed that a purchase of arsenic had been found and would be proved against him.

They knew that, on 9 March, he had asked Dr Richard W. Muller, of 10 East 58th Street, to recommend him to a pharmacist, as he wanted, he said, to purchase some arsenic to destroy a cat. Dr Muller had kindly telephoned to Timmerman's drug store, at 802 Lexington Avenue, explained that Waite was a dentist, and said that it would be all right to let him have the arsenic. The assistant at Timmerman's, after an unsuccessful attempt to persuade Waite that strychnine was more efficacious for the destruction of animals, had sold him ninety grains of white arsenic and made him sign the record book.

Thus did Arthur acquire his supply of what the French in their cynicism call *poudre de succession*: inheritance powder.

Faced with this alarming piece of evidence, he blustered a little, then came out with the pathetically futile yarn that he had done it out of kindly consideration for his father-in-law. The old man had been grieving terribly over the loss of his wife. Life no longer had any meaning for him and he had repeatedly said that all he wanted was to die and join her. After a long resistance, out of sheer pity, he had given in to his father-in-law's insistence, bought the package of arsenic, and given it to him. He had not administered any of the poison. He had not seen Mr Peck take it. All that he had done that was wrong — if it *was* wrong — was to give, out of mercy, a desperately sad old man the means to end his sadness.

'Of course, you don't believe me,' said Waite to DA Swann. 'I suppose I shall go to the electric chair.'

Yet once more, he proved an accurate prophet.

The DA had another nasty surprise up his sleeve. He knew all about Mr Eugene Oliver Kane.

To appreciate the devastating importance of this piece of police knowledge, it is necessary to know that soon after his last return from Grand Rapids, Waite had had a caller at Riverside Drive. Nervously twiddling his hat in his hand, John Potter, the respectful, black-suited undertaker who had undertaken the preparation of Mr Peck for his last earthly journey, was ushered by Dora into Waite's somewhat surprised presence.

Apologetically, suppliantly, Mr Potter (surely well named for his avocation: he sounds an appropriate member of a pack of *Un*happy Family cards) politely requested that his bill should be paid.

'What's the hurry? You know the money's safe, don't you?' snapped a for once unsmiling Waite.

'It's really Mr Kane, sir, the embalmer. He thinks he might not get his money.'

'Not get his money! Why ever not?'

'Well, sir, there's talk. Some idea that arsenic may have been used.'

Waite knew that it was against the law for arsenic to be put into any preservative mixtures employed upon human bodies. He also knew that arsenic would be found in Mr Peck's body if it were examined.

'I think I'd better see Mr Kane,' he said.

And he had done just that. Gone round to see him. Made no bones about the unusual undertaking he required from the embalmer. He was, he explained, in a bit of a hole. He was being jobbed (English: framed), made the victim of circumstances, falsely accused. Kane was able to help him. Would he? He wanted a kind of miracle: to change the water of embalming fluid into the wine of emblaming fluid. He wanted Kane to testify that there was arsenic in the fluid with which Mr Peck's body was treated. Favours don't come cheap in New York. He knew that. Kane would be looked after, well rewarded . . . .

The embalmer named his price. There was a brief haggle. Nine thousand dollars was agreed. The bargain struck. A further meeting arranged.

Waite, who by now suspected that his movements were being watched, suggested a casual encounter next day in a cigar store. There, Waite had stepped into a phone booth and pushed a fat roll of bills into Kane's pocket, instructing him to prepare a sample of the fluid, stuffed full of arsenic, and send it down to the DA pdq.

Waite's suspicions were correct. He *was* being followed.

Taken into custody, grilled, the embalmer quivered and quailed, broke down immediately, blubbering and blurting: 'Waite told me the DA was going to ask me for a specimen of my embalming fluid. Asked me to send it doctored with arsenic.'

Yes, yes, he had taken the money.

'He gave me a big roll of bills. I was so scared I could hardly tell where I was. I stood there with the money in my hand. Waite told me, "For God's sake get that stuff out of sight." I put it back in my pocket. Then I went right home.

I was so nervous about the money that my wife noticed it. She got to worrying me and at last made me go to a doctor to find out if I was sick. I knew all right, but I didn't tell her. I shook like a leaf every now and then when I got to thinking about the money in the bureau drawer. Then I took it to Long Island and buried it.'

He had not, he insisted, put anything into the sample of the embalming fluid of the kind injected into Mr Peck's corpse. 'I made it up just the same as I always make it — of formaldehyde, glycerine and sodium phosphate.'

The sum of $7800 was dug up from the place on Long Island indicated by the chastened Mr Kane. What had become of the other $1200 is a minor mystery never officially solved.

It should perhaps be added that Mr Kane's own record was less than immaculate. On more than one occasion he had been suspected of extending a (self) helping hand to well-heeled clients 'in a bit of a hole'.

Awaking from his sulphonal slumbers, and his dream of making himself a millionaire, Arthur Warren Waite, fully aware now of his predicament and the overwhelming evidence against him, dreamt up a new scenario.

He would play the part of Dr Jekyll and Mr Hyde. He would go nap on schizophrenia.[1] He would call into evidence The Man From Egypt.

Arthur Warren Waite was brought to trial in the middle of May 1916.

He pleaded Not Guilty. A somewhat delicate decision, you might think, in view of the circumstance that, faced by the DA with the discovery of his purchase of arsenic and the bribing of Kane, he had, as we have already seen, cracked and 'coughed', written then to a New York newspaper making public confession of his guilt of the deaths of his in-laws, expressing contrition and his entire willingness to pay

1. The reference here is to the psychotic disease, not to be confused with the popular misconception of schizophrenia as a condition of so-called 'split personality'.

the supreme penalty, and completed the confessional hat-trick by going on to provide the prosecutor with further and better particulars.

He would live — but not for long — to regret the hastiness of his impulsive catharsis. He would have been better advised to hold his tongue and embark upon the usual plea-bargaining trade-off of a life for a death — i.e. a State's-time-and-cash-saving plea of guilty of felonious death-dealing in return for a life-sparing life sentence. Now, though, the social and moral atrocity of his merciless despatch of the amiable old couple having switched on a savage retaliatory instinct in the breasts of the just, the wretched Waite would not have been permitted to bargain-plead guilty, would have been afforded no chance to short-circuit the electric chair — so that perhaps that 'delicate decision' to make a not-guilty plea was not his decision at all, but a law enforcement. And thus, deprived of his best defence — that of guilt — he adopted the second best: that of contriving a guilty-but-by-reason-of-obvious-insanity verdict.

This would iron out many puzzlements in his conduct and comportment.

A man being tried for double murder might reasonably be expected to exhibit some small signs of perturbation — a slight hint of strain here, a visible shaft of anxiety there. Not so, relaxed, urbane, quizzically amused 'Dr' Waite. His perpetual smile seemed always poised upon the lip's edge of laughter. His inappropriate gaiety had first bubbled over way back at the time they were picking the jury. There had been one prospective juryman who, on challenge, had been asked if he was opposed to capital punishment. 'Not in *this* case,' he had replied emphatically, and the laughter of no one in the court-room rang louder than Waite's. He was to laugh again, and heartily, many, many times during the presentation of the prosecution's case.

On the day Waite took the stand, the courtroom was packed wall-to-wall. All eyes became cameras, zooming in on the good-looking, 'film star' young man, with the small, almost feminine (they were so described) features, as he rose from his seat at the table beside his counsel, Walter R. Duell. He had groomed himself with especial care for the occasion. He moved swiftly forward across the floor. He appeared eager to reach the witness-chair.

It was pantomime time!

He was to play the Court jester — the *not-so-mad* Fool.

And make no mistake: for all its integral beastliness, there *is* a certain amount of comedy, black comedy, in the case.

Waite, 'with the air of a man relating a diverting story at a cocktail party', was, as it were, button-holing the jury. A nod-nod, wink-wink performance worthy of a Hollywood Great.

First of all, Counsellor Duell took his client step by embarrassing step over the bemired terrain of his early life. How he had cheated at examinations at Ann Arbor by stealing the laboratory work of a more gifted student and passing it in, and off, as his own. How he had stolen a thousand dollars from a fellow-student's trunk, and only saved his bacon by its shamefaced restoration. He confessed, too, his subsequent small thefts and expulsion from his fraternity at the University of Michigan and his hefty 'appropriations' from his employers in South Africa, so that he might have a worthwhile, easy-come-easy-go fortune to bring home to Grand Rapids with him. He admitted also to snivelling little thefts from the purse of his trusting mother-in-law.

To all these shaming, blush-making thefts and wrong-doings Waite confessed without let or hindrance; no diminution of the brightness of that smile, no smallest falter in his amiable, punctilious politeness. In short, he did it all with the true psychopath's lack of what the psychiatrists call affect. That is to say, without any token of the existence of embarrassment, guilt or remorse.

Having thus painlessly submitted to the laying surgically bare of these unhealthy infrastructures of his life history, Waite was now about to be led on to tell of infinitely greater and graver obliquities and iniquities. The more terrible his story, the more coolly he would tell it, and the greater, hopefully, would be the chance that the jury would think him a madman.

To this end, he refuted none of the testimony given against him. Rather, aided and abetted by his attorney, he strove to support and embellish it, to blacken himself still further.

Yes ... yes, everything the prosecution said about him was true. He was an even more outrageous and contradictory character than they had made out.

Yes ... he had married Clara Louise Peck so as to become rich and independent. Life without money was torture, and not worth living. To get the Peck fortune, or at least a large slice of it, into his hands, he would have to dispose of his wife's parents, her aunt — perhaps his wife herself.

When he had first made these admissions to the police, his stunned interrogator had asked him: 'Are you crazy?' That was before Waite had decided to play-act just that. 'I think not,' he had replied, 'unless it's crazy to want money.'

Given time, he added, he would almost certainly have murdered Clara. 'She was not my equal in anything. When I had got rid of her, I meant to find a more beautiful wife.'

The motive was clear. Arthur Warren Waite was poisoning off the Pecks for cash, and, as my father, a learned attorney, was wont to observe, money is the purest of all motives.

Counsel decided to hammer the point home. Make sure. 'Why do you say you wanted to kill them?' he asked.

Waite came right up to proof. Hit it bang on the head. 'For their money. I've always needed lots of money, and it has never worried me how I got hold of it.'

The perfect 'split-personality' answer. There, laconically, spoke two people.

The honest man: 'For their money.'
The psychopath: 'Never worried me how I got hold of it.'

There was the debonair dentist, far from down in the mouth, up there 'singing' like a man carried away, possessed, moved to testify at a breast-beating Moody & Sankey revivalist meeting – or a classic clinical specimen of what Dr William Sargant described as dissociation phenomenon.

The delivery of his testimony was, like the performances of Elizabethan actors, punctuated by stage-front asides. Further incontrovertible pointers to his quintessential psychopathy. Asides about himself and the world (revolving) around him. Such confidences as that he had always considered himself to be 'attractive and charming', and, spoken in accents disarming, 'Everyone liked me'.

The extraordinary narration began. It was like nothing a jury had ever listened to before. Brutal, if not brutish, honesty. Devastating directness.

As befitted one who sought refuge in a defence of complete moral imbecility, Waite began with cheery admissions of various attempts to murder Aunt Catherine Peck. To that end he had gone to the Cornell University Medical School and there persuaded William Weber, an attendant, who had no authority to pass out such merchandise of death, to give him test-tube cultures of various pathogenic micro-organisms. For 'persuaded' read 'bribed'. For 'give' read 'sell'.

'I gave her repeated doses of germs. Then some arsenic. And after that I put some ground glass in her marmalade, but she thought it was sand and returned it to the grocer. I also injected live germs into a can of fish before presenting it to her.'

He had, however, temporarily abandoned his attempt to wipe out Aunt Catherine when Mrs Peck came to stay. He could not see the point of murdering the aunt when there were much richer pickings – or should it be 'peckings'? – to be obtained by murdering his mother-in-law. As Auden and MacNeice point out in their Icelandic correspondence:

Adventurers, though, must take things as they find
them,
And look for pickings where the pickings are.
The drives of love and hunger are behind them,
They can't afford to be particular.

Waite went on to tell of the murder of Mrs Peck.
She had been easy to kill.

'I started poisoning her from the very first meal after she
arrived. I gave her six assorted tubes of pneumonia and
diphtheria germs and influenza virus in her food. She then
became ill and took to her bed.'

After she had been ill for some days, Waite had volunteered to sit up with her one night, and when, later, the
time came to give her a dose of the medicine prescribed for
her by Dr Porter: 'I ground up twelve five-grain veronal
tablets and gave that to her in solution in her medicine.'

'And then what did you do after you had given your
mother-in-law the fatal dose of poison?' asked Counsel.

'Why, I guess I went back to sleep, of course. I woke up
in the small hours and went along to my mother-in-law's
room. She was dead. I came quietly out of the room and
went back to bed again so that it would be my wife who
would discover the body.'

He darted a boyish smile to the jurors. It was slaughter
most suave.

The jurors, who had patently regarded Waite with some
horror at the start of his evidence, had, as it progressed,
become infected by his charm. That unwavering smile, that
unwearying politeness, those faultless manners, had all
been quietly and insidiously achieving their intended effect.

Now Waite was speaking again, using that soothing,
melodiously British-accented voice of his like a musical
instrument. In the same suave, emotionless way, he was
gently describing his weeks-long struggle to kill his
father-in-law.

Old Mr Peck had been much tougher than his wife.

'I gave him larges doses of about everything I had. I used
to insert tubes of typhoid, diphtheria and pneumonia

germs and influenza virus in his soup and rice-puddings – but,' said Waite ruefully, 'they didn't seem to affect him.

'Then I tried tubercular sputum. I procured a nasal spray into which I put it, and induced him to use that, but it didn't work. I also gave him a throat spray, laced with germs. Nothing seemed to have the slightest effect on him.

'When that didn't work either, I got a lot of calomel and fed him that in order to weaken his system so that he could not resist the germs, but it failed. He recovered every time.'

But Arthur, as we have already noted, was a try, try, try again man.

'I tried many other things in the hope that he would succumb. I would get him to go out and expose himself to draughts. I would open his bedroom window in the hope that it would give him pneumonia, or at least that he would catch a cold. For the same reason I dampened his bed sheets, put water in his rubbers [gum-boots], and wet the seat of the automobile before taking him out for a drive. None of these things worked either.'

Waite had toyed with the idea of faking a car accident.

'I tried to get him out in an automobile with me. My idea was to stall at the top of a hill with him in the back seat. I planned to jump and let him go over a cliff in the car. I couldn't do that either.

'Once, I got some hydrochloric acid and put it in the radiator in his room, expecting the fumes would affect him. They didn't.

'One night I turned on the gas in his room, but the superintendent came up and told me about the leak. I had to shut it off.'

Other interim attempts included letting off the occasional modest-sized canister or two of chlorine gas in the bedroom – 'I hoped the gas would weaken his resistance like it did with the soldiers at the front. I used to put some stuff on the electric heater so that if he noticed a funny smell I could say it was something burning' – and feeding him a mixture of burnt fly-papers and veronal.

Incredibly, the sheer *bonhomie* of the narrator began to

communicate itself to his listeners, as he sat hour after hour in the witness-chair, head erect, emotionless, reciting in an incongruously bland and happy manner a hideous account of horrendous deeds. The charm seemed to ooze over and defuse the explosive cruelty of the words of his blood-curdling tale of viciously calculated murder. Almost without realising it, members of the jury found themselves nodding in understanding, swapping smiles in sympathy with him, at the irksome difficulties he had encountered in destroying 'Dad'. The odd juror even gave vent to the occasional muffled giggle. Undoubtedly, there was in it an element of the hysterical laughter-at-a-funeral syndrome.

Finally, Waite had given his stubbornly surviving victim arsenic.

'I gave him a lot in his food.'

Indeed he had. He spiked Mr Peck's egg-nog with it. He sprinkled the shiny white powder liberally in soup, oatmeal, rice-pudding, milk and tea, in piecemeal poisonings until he had used up the whole of his ninety-grain purchase on — or in — his father-in-law. Yet, even after a single helping of eighteen grains — at least six times the normally fatal dose and enough to knock a team of draught-horses off their hooves — the formidable old gentleman was still alive. Albeit in a bad way.

'On the night of 12 March, he was in great pain and groaning. I had been left to watch by his bedside while my wife got some rest. He was, as I said, groaning with pain and begging for something that would relieve it.'

How this relief was provided — it was lip-twitching, rib-tickling funny — Waite went on to recount to his 'audience' of jurors with the same smiling sang-froid: 'Clara kept various drugs and medicaments about the house. In her medicine-chest there was a small bottle of chloroform. I saturated a cloth with some of it and went over to him and said, "Dad, here's some ether and ammonia which will relieve your pain."'

Instead of his usual professional 'Open wide', Waite crooned soothingly, 'Breathe deep.' Mr Peck breathed

123

deep. Soon he would breathe his last. He felt relieved. The agony receded. His pain and weakness were such that he continued to inhale the numbing vapour until he became unconscious ... unconsciously embracing death's ultimate anodyne.

Then ... swift as a rattlesnake but without the serpent's warning ... Waite struck. Poured more chloroform on the cloth, repositioned it, pressed it, moulded it, around the limp old man's nose and mouth. He fetched a pillow then and with its feather-down touch administered the *coup de dis-grâce*, holding it with steel-vice grip over the face. He did not release it until John E. Peck was dead.

At the time when, after his suicide gesture or attempt, Waite was questioned by the DA in hospital, he had at once admitted that he had given his father-in-law arsenic. The DA had asked: 'Have you any accomplices?'

'Only this other fellow,' the self-accused man had replied. A throw-away line delivered with elaborate carelessness.

'What other fellow?'

'The Man from Egypt.'

Encouraged, Waite carefully elaborated. 'He's always been inside me ever since I can remember. He has made me do things against my will. He made me take up the study of germs, as, if I used them, I wouldn't be detected. I was compelled against my will to put them in my father-in-law's food. Try as I would, I couldn't get rid of my murderous other self. Often I've gone for long walks and fought against the evil one, and tried to run away from him, but he was so fleet of foot he always caught me up.'

Me, I'm from Missouri, as American Doubting Thomases say, about the Man from Egypt — but so earnestly did Waite tell his story that it was partly believed. On the witness-stand he made no attempt to hide the appallingly evil personality of The Man from Egypt. On the contrary, only too eagerly did he call into evidence the *alter ego* who, he stoutly maintained, had compelled him to contemplate and to commit crimes which shocked even case-hardened New York.

'Did this Egyptian make you kill Mr Peck?' Waite was asked.

'When my father-in-law came to stay with us, I wanted to help him all I could. Then The Man from Egypt said Mr Peck was too old to live, that he ought to die, and if he did die I wouldn't have to worry about money. He brushed aside all my arguments. When Mr Peck had first visited us, The Man from Egypt made me spray his throat with germs; but though they made him ill, they didn't kill him. I was ordered on his second visit to use arsenic as it was quicker. I was to put it in his soup and tea and egg-nog. I did my best, but The Man from Egypt was in control. Try as I would, I found it impossible to get rid of him.'

Then, solemnly, Waite told the Court: 'But now that he has forced me to do these things, he has left me, and for the first time I feel that my soul is free. He seemed to leave me last night and he hasn't returned again today to torture me with his evil suggestions.' He looked around with shining eyes importuning the Court's sympathy.

A nice piece of foundation laying – or lying – for future psychotherapeutic 'miracles' which would return him 'cured', to live a full, rich and happy life back once more in the world of the normal. For the nonce, however, Waite declared that he was a 'split personality', and that the half of him that drove him to murder was an Ancient Egyptian. Reincarnation was a topic to which he referred frequently – although he does seem to have got his wires crossed a little, for reincarnation, 'split-personality', and multiple personality are by no means synonymous. 'I believe that, although my body lives in America, my soul lives in secret Egypt. It is The Man from Egypt who has committed these foul crimes.'

All this preternaturally serious talk of The Man from Egypt had exactly the effect that Waite foresaw. It was so wild that it seemed as though only a madman could so present it.

(The laboured psychological alibi – the *real me* was somewhere else at the material time – falls tediously echoing upon the modern ear. Seventy-odd years on, one is reminded of so many others — such as that of Ken Bianchi, one of the Californian Hillside Strangler's hands — the other Strangler's hand was Bianchi's cousin Angelo Buono — and his multiple personality act, claiming to off-load the blame on to his co-corporeal inhabitant, 'Steve Walker', the vicious, unprincipled 'Violent Man'.)

When the prosecution pressed Waite for details of his other life by the banks of the Nile, he was remarkably unforthcoming. He mentioned Caesar and Cleopatra, and the palm-trees and the pyramids, which latter he characterised with the highly un-Ancient Egyptian descriptive 'voluptuous'.

The whole purpose of this charade was to implant in the minds of the jury the idea that a man as intelligent, as civilised, as the delightful doctor had clearly established himself to be, could by no stretch of the imagination have carried out the heinous crimes to which he had so freely admitted — and at the same time be sane.

And just to help them along, Waite would suddenly inter-ject out of the crazy blue some such observation as 'What-ever they may say of me, I pride myself on being kind and always giving water to flowers so they will not die'.

The wiseacres, cynical newspapermen and seasoned lawyers, could *see* the plea of insanity approaching over the near horizon.

(As in the Gary Heidnik case [1988] — murders committed in Philadelphia, trial in Pittsburgh following change-of-venue motion — when the enormity, the sheer bizarre horror, of the crimes demands it, the best defence is admission of guilt with an insanity plea in mitigation tacked on to it.

> Any person who puts dog-food and human remains in a food processor and calls it a gourmet meal and feeds it to others is out to lunch.
>
> Counsellor A. Charles Peruto, Jr
> Defence Counsel for Gary Heidnik)

Waite's attorney then produced psychiatrists — alienists, as it was then the fashion to call them — to provide expert testimony that a man who could do, and afterwards talk about, such deeds could not be held to be sane within the meaning of the law. The State called alienists of its own who said that Waite, having displayed normal responses to diagnostic tests to which they had subjected him, must be adjudged sane.

One psychiatrist told the Court that Waite had informed him: 'Miss Catherine Peck said that when she remembered how beautifully I had sung hymns in church while my wife's relations were visiting us, she could not believe that I committed the crimes. It was my *real* self that appeared then.'

Dr Jeliffe, the leading alienist for the prosecution, said: 'In my opinion, the prisoner was sane and knew the nature and quality of his act. He was fully aware of all the phases of his crime. In my opinion, he is an average man, somewhat superficial, inclined to be snobbish, and of no great intellectual attainments.'

The judge finally ruled in favour of the prosecution alienists' findings. (He had, it has been scandalously asserted, been 'in part swayed by his irritation over Waite's constant smile'.) The trial moved on.

Very much the man of the world, Waite cocked an amused ear as witness after witness unfolded a black tale against him. Occasionally he emitted a good-humoured chuckle. He heard unperturbed of the discovery in his apartment of books concerning the usage and effects of arsenic, with pages tell-tale marked and turned down at the corner. (Poisoners seem to be constitutionally careless in such matters — *videlicet*: the *Donellan, Bartlett,* and *Fullam-Clark* cases.) He heard accounts of his two attempts to bribe witnesses: Dora, the family maid — and Eugene Kane.

The appearance on the witness-stand of the small, bespectacled embalmer, twitching and peeking like some small disturbed pest animal, seemed to tickle Waite, who burst into frank laughter several times during Kane's testificatory twitterings.

To be honest, Kane did not cut too impressive a figure under examination. The nuclear shiftiness of the man peeped through. He had just explained how Waite had come out of a telephone booth and 'pushed a roll of notes in my pocket'.

> *Prosecutor*: Did you know what it was for?
>
> *Kane*: No, I thought it must be for something I had done.
>
> *Prosecutor*: He told you, though, didn't he?
>
> *Kane*: He said: 'Put some arsenic into that fluid and send it down to the District Attorney.'
>
> *Prosecutor*: Were you nervous?
>
> *Kane*: I certainly was.
>
> *Prosecutor*: Did you count the money when you got home?'
>
> *Kane*: No. I tried to but I was too nervous. I saw some fifties and some hundreds, that's all.
>
> *Prosecutor*: Any large bills?
>
> *Kane*: Yes, sir. Two five-hundred-dollar bills. I hid the money in a closet. I tried to count it two or three times. Finally, I went to Long Island and buried it. I went to Greenport, 'way to the east of the island.'

Clara Waite, called to the stand, told the Court of her surprise when, after her mother's unexpected death, her husband had said that it had been Mrs Peck's last wish to be cremated — 'It was the first I'd heard of it'. On the last night of her mother's life, Clara had heard her heavy breathing. Arthur had said Mother had a very bad cold. In the morning she had found her dead.

On the night of 12 March, she had heard Arthur, who had been sitting up with her father, ring the doctor. Later, he came into the bedroom in his robe, looking disturbed, and said: 'I don't think Dad's too good.' She had rushed to her father's room, but he was already dead. Once again, she was surprised when Arthur told her: 'It was Dad's last wish to be cremated.' Nevertheless,she had accepted his word.

The surprise of the trial came on the third day, when the Hardwickes, mother and daughter, gave evidence.

The daughter, Elizabeth, tall, attractive, composed, testified that it was she who had sent the cryptic telegram signed 'K. Adams' (the name of a friend) at her mother's behest.

The mother said that after being told by her brother, Dr Cornell, of the chilly reception given to him when he had called to offer the Waites condolences, she fell to thinking. She remembered meeting the doctor and his 'nurse' in the dining-room at the Hotel Plaza. She realised that Arthur would now be in control of a very large sum of money. She became somehow convinced that he was responsible for the two deaths and she had asked her daughter to send the pseudonymous telegram. Had it not been for that telegram, Mr Peck's body would have been cremated and there would have been no evidence of his having been poisoned.

It was the disclosures of Margaret Horton when she went on to the witness-stand which effectively put an end to any thin chance Waite might have had of bypassing death row.

And this was what did it. Mrs Horton recalled that at the time when rumours were thick as midges in the air, Arthur had invited her to his laboratory, where he had shown her 'tiny germs wriggling under a microscope'. That was when she had brought everything out into the open by asking him, point-blank, 'You didn't really do it, did you, Arthur? And he had answered, 'Yes. It's true. I did.'

Then, after his arrest, he had sent her a letter which, on counsel's advice, she had destroyed. Under pressure, she was able to remember the following damning words from it: 'If they prove it, I suppose it will mean *la chaise*, but I hope and expect to spend a while in detention as an imbecile, and then I'll be free again to join you.' It was this, perhaps more than anything else, which led Justice Shearn to rule that Waite was not an imbecile.

Since Margaret Horton had been identified as the woman who had accompanied Waite on the occasion when he bought the germs at Cornell Medical School, it had for a while seemed advisable for her to retain her own attorney, with the equivalent of an English watching brief, but she was never seriously considered as being involved in the murders.

One entire day towards the end of the trial was taken up with a series of witnesses paying cordial tribute to the gentle heart and genteel manners of the immaculate Arthur.

Indeed, literally dozens of people who *thought* they knew the good doctor really well were truly flabbergasted. He was *so* nice, *so* kind. What's more, he had a strong streak of piety in him. All through the time that he was *alleged* to be in the process of poisoning his relatives, he had been attending church regularly. There wasn't an ounce of malice in him. All he ever wanted was to be happy and have those around him happy too. If all this that was being said against him was true ... why, then, he really must be a Jekyll and Hyde.

After his arrest, his wife had declared: 'I was so shocked and amazed that I could not believe all those stories about his various affairs to be true. It seems impossible that a man who has been so uniformly kind and gentle to me, and apparently so loyal, could be guilty of the crimes with which he is charged.'

Margaret Horton testified: 'Dr Waite had an extraordinarily kind heart. He loved all the fine sentiments and the beautiful things of life. He used to say to me, "Margaret, when you sing, you make me weep, because you make me think of beautiful things." He loved music. It was that love of music that drew us together.'

Now the doctor was facing the music alone.

A modicum less rosy was the testimonial proffered by Percival Peck. 'I know that Arthur is guilty. The electric chair will be too good for him. Even if he were tortured, his death would never bring back my beloved parents or pay for his horrible deeds. I will do all in my power to see that he is found guilty and executed. He is surely entitled to no consideration whatever. I am convinced that he married my sister with but one idea, and that was to get her money. Even before her mother died, he predicted an untimely death for us all. We believed him to be a surgeon, and when Mother died we suspected nothing. Even when the news of Father's death came, we did not suspect until we got that telegram. I am sure, if it had not been for that, my sister and my aunt would have died next.'

Percy Peck remained adamantine to the end. He approached the prosecution just before the trial and told them: 'I have only one favour to ask, and that is that I have a seat through every minute of the trial near that man, so that I can see the last gleam of hope gradually fade from his face.'

The trial of Arthur Warren Waite was, as a matter of fact, much shorter than are the majority of sensational American murder trials. It lasted only five days.

Counsel for the defence's final speech was powerful and persuasive.

'Waite has told you the truth. There is no part of his story that is not true. He has no moral sense whatever. What are we going to do with such a man as this? You would not send to the electric chair an idiot, a lunatic or a child. On the other hand, we cannot permit such a man as Waite to be at large. We must remove him from society by placing him in an institution.'

That brought the judge down on him like a ton of bricks.

'You are not,' Justice Shearn told the jury, 'concerned at all with the question of the punishment of this man. The question raised by the defendant's counsel of what to do with such a man is not the question at all. The law determines what shall be done. Your function is to determine the facts, so that the law may operate. Do not get it into your heads that you are called upon to determine anything but the facts. Juries have no right to set up standards of what constitutes right and wrong, and no right to discuss how the law shall deal with a man like this. You must not attempt to usurp the functions of the Legislature. In this case no claim is made that the defendant did it in the heat of passion. On the contrary, he himself admits premeditation, intent and a motive. No matter what the defendant has confessed, you must remember that the burden still rests upon the prosecution to establish his guilt beyond a reasonable doubt. The defendant is entitled to have the case determined on the facts and not on what he says.'

Justice Shearn's direction in regard to the issue of legal insanity is a model of clarity and sound judicial sense: 'You might infer, from arguments of counsel and some of the evidence, that you are here to hold a medical clinic. That is not so at all. It would be absurd to ask twelve laymen to determine whether from the medical point of view a man is sane or insane, especially as men learned in the profession do not agree on the matter. The question is not whether he is sane, but whether he was responsible under the tests prescribed by law. That is: *Did he know the nature and quality of the act, and know it was wrong?* That is not a test for experts but for men of common sense. Moral indifference is not insanity. The claim that the defendant was weak in will-power and that he was unable to resist suggestions like those from "The Man from Egypt", has also been passed on by the higher courts, who have held that, no matter what medical authority there may be for such a claim, it cannot be assented to by the courts. Indulgence in evil passion weakens the will-power and at the same time the sense of responsibility.'

For all the jokes and smiles, the becking and beaming, when it came to the decision-time, the jury proved to be not impressionable. The thistledown of charm wore thin against the spikier teazels of reality. It took them just twenty minutes, and one ballot, to reach a verdict of Guilty.

An odd-ball to the end, Waite greeted his conviction and sentence to death with a sigh, and said: 'What a relief.'

He was quickly taken to Sing Sing by train, and was reported as being, on both the New York and Sing Sing railroad station platforms, 'almost playful, saying that he was going to a nice quiet place, where, later, he would have a nice long rest'.

From the end of May 1916, until the following April, Waite waited in his nice quiet place upriver.

'He was,' wrote Edward H. Smith in a memorable passage,[1] 'pleasant and condescending to the rough men in the prison house with him. He let them know that though they were in death the same, in life there were gulfs and chasms between them — even in that dim half-life in the shadow of the chair. And the undermen of the death house, used to humility and obsequiousness, accepted the snobbery with pathetic submission.'

On 3 April 1917, The Court of Appeals, having found nothing to say on the question of guilt, affirmed the conviction without opinion stated, and decided that Waite's sentence must stand. Thereupon, the trial judge, wishing not to appear overhasty, delayed a month before setting the new date of execution for the week beginning Monday, 21 May.

Meanwhile, Waite's attorney applied to Governor Whitman to have a panel of doctors examine Waite to determine the issue of his sanity. This Commission in Lunacy in due course reported that he was perfectly sane. Governor Whitman washed his hands of the matter, and the news was conveyed to the prisoner in Sing Sing that he must die.

Waite merely smiled, hummed a tune, and said: 'Is that so?' The condemned man then pulled out of the hat a gesture well matching his court performance of a year earlier. He sat down in the death cell and penned the following note to Warden Moyer.

Dear Sir,

In one of the newspapers today is the statement: 'A.W. Waite to die next week.' On inquiry I learn that you have power to name the day. I am sure you would not be averse to obliging me if you found it possible and reasonable to do so, and I wondered if we could not arrange for Monday of next week. There really is a reason for asking this, although

1. *Famous American Poison Mysteries*, Hurst & Blackett, London, 1927.

I will not trouble you with explanations. I would be very grateful indeed for this favour.

Yours respectfully,
ARTHUR WARREN WAITE

Tidings of this latest piece of 'nerve', reaching the public beyond the Sing Sing fences, evoked gasps of surprise, edged with grudging admiration.

Warden Moyer did not oblige. He fixed the night of Thursday, 24 May, for Waite's electrocution.

During that last waiting year of his curtailed life, Waite had only two regular visitors: his brother Frank and his attorney, Walter Duell. Iron-nerved, iron-willed, keeping himself to himself, he had killed the lonely hours reading — the prose of Poe, Ibsen, Maeterlinck and the Bible, the poetry of Keats and Browning.

He was writing poetry, too. He dedicated one poem to himself — an address to his body by his soul after death.

> And thou art dead, dear comrade,
> In whom I dwelt a time,
> With whom I strolled through star-kissed bowers
> Of fragrant jessamine.
> And thou wert weak, O comrade,
> Thyself in self did fail,
> And now the stars are turned to tears
> And sobs the nightingale.
> And though I now must leave you,
> The same old songs I'll sing,
> And o'er yon hill the same soft dew
> Will spread its silver wing.
> Across the fields, among the stars,
> I now must go alone,
> Your spirit now will roam afar,
> And leave you, friend, alone.

He never wearied of talking about himself. Another good psychopathic trait.

'My life consisted of lying, cheating, stealing and killing, but my personality was that of a gentleman, and I went for music, art and poetry.

'I was looking over the Ten Commandments and I found I had broken all but one. The one about profanity. I have never been profane.'

He continued to display right up to the fall of the curtain that curious double personality.

When the hour struck, he said his farewells, unmoved by the grief of his brother, unconcerned about the illness of his distraught mother. That old psychopathy had him in its spell.

His last evening on earth he sat reading — the Bible, Keats, Browning. He also wrote to Amos Squire, the Sing Sing prison doctor, carefully sealing the folded sheet of paper in a double envelope.

In full, tight control of himself, he was fleetingly annoyed when guards arrived to escort him to the death chamber. They had interrupted his last reading of Robert Browning.

> Life's a little thing!
> Such as it is, then,
> pass life pleasantly....

It was shortly after 11 pm, as, composed and unafraid, Waite strolled down the corridor to the execution chamber. His calmness intact, he waved as he passed other inhabitants of death row, a temporarily chastened tenantry, and called out to them, 'Goodbye, boys!' and sauntered on, that boyish smile of old still playing about his somewhat effeminate lips, to keep his appointment in a Samarra called Sing Sing with Marksman Death.

He hesitated, but only for a split second, upon the threshold of the grim place of the chair, registering the uninviting aspect of its embrace. Wrote one who was present:

> I saw him step into the room. I saw him advance the few steps to the chair. Waite blinked at the glare of the lights. He waved his hand. There were twenty people in the room. He was strapped in the chair.

While he was being pinioned, Dr Squire approached and asked if he had any last word he wished conveyed to

135

anyone. 'No thank you, doctor, there is no one to whom I care to leave a farewell message.'

The psychopath's typical lonely exit.

As the electrodes were being fixed about his body and clamped to his shaven-patched scalp, he looked around and spoke his last words ever.

'Is this all there is to it?'

Within seconds, two shocks of two thousand volts had crashed through his body ... a taut jerking ... a stray will-o'-the-wisp of smoke from the burnt flesh ... and he was dead.

He was twenty-nine years old.

American law requires that an autopsy must be carried out on an executed person at once, and this is usually done in a small chamber situated directly behind the room in which the execution has taken place.

In Waite's case, the post-mortem revealed evidence of an old meningitis on the right cerebellum, probably due to a fall or a blow to the head in childhood. The doctors did not think that it could in any way have affected his sanity. He was found, too, to have an abnormally large heart — enlarged perhaps as a result of his athletic activities. He was otherwise normal, no disease, and said to have been exceptionally well developed physically.

When, the autopsy over, Dr Squire opened the double-sealed letter from Waite, he found a curious content. Upon a single sheet of paper — a sort of visiting-card of his stay on earth — Waite had written:

> Call us with morning faces,
> Eager to labour, eager to be happy ....

That was all.

Two weeks after the execution, Waite's widow filed suit to recover the $7000 remaining of the $9000 that her husband had paid to Kane. Three years later, Clara remarried in Pasadena.

Margaret Horton was offered, and accepted, a ten-week contract to sing and play the piano at Loew's 175th Street

Theatre, New York City — an engagement which, speculated the cynical, had at least as much to do with her connection with the sensational Waite affair as with the artistic attraction of her reportedly 'militant contralto' voice.

There was, it turns out, even in the central figure of this criminous drama, less than meets the eye. Waite is something of a disappointment. He was not, it transpires upon conscientious investigation, the innovative genius, the only begetter of the method, the genie of the germ.

Back in 1912, Henri Girard, a Frenchman and 'flashy insurance tout', had pressed *bacillus typhosus* — the typhoid germ — into homicidal service.

Yet he, too, had been bested by an even earlier pioneer of bacteriological homicide, the German germ slayer, Karl Ropf.

Closer in time to Waite, and quite possibly his role-model, was Dr Bennett Clark Hyde, of Kansas City.

For days before his execution, Waite was in communication with a woman spiritualist to whom he faithfully promised that after he was dead he would return and give her some message to prove the existence of a world beyond the electric chair. But after the last crackle, sizzle, stop — the rest was silence. Predictably, he let her down. Psychopathologically speaking, *plus ça change.* . . .

Murder For Lust of Killing*

F. TENNYSON JESSE

KILLING FOR KILLING'S SAKE is an apparently motiveless motive. Yet this class is a wide and varied field. It is possible to distinguish two divisions, which we may call *A* and *B*.

In Division *A* come the murders where the satisfaction of lust is in the actual killing, without any sexual connection with the victim.

In Division *B* come the murders committed at the same time as or directly after the sexual act, not for the purpose of concealing outrage — which would be a murder of elimination — but as part of the sexual gratification.

Occasionally, as in the case of the man known to the prostitutes of Vienna as 'The Chicken Killer', a man may know of the tendency to murder, at this moment, within himself, and may arrange for its gratification more or less harmlessly. On the other hand, there is the case of Vidal, the French killer of women, who had a horror of blood, and could not kill a chicken himself, though he was a poultry merchant, and yet he murdered four women during his uncontrollable frenzies in the space of one month.

In the murders of Division *A* there is nearly always to be found a commingling of the power mania with the lust of

---

* One of the six motives for murder postulated by Miss Jesse, the others being: for gain, for revenge, for elimination, for jealousy, and from conviction. Her essay on Constance Kent, used by her to exemplify the motive of revenge, appears in an earlier volume of this series of anthologies, *The Country House Murders*.

138

killing; especially is this the case with poisoners, and consequently their crimes are more subtle in their motives than those which come into Division *B*.

Jegado, Van der Linden, and Zwanziger all suffered from power-mania. Feuerbach, the great Bavarian judge, said of Zwanziger: 'Her attachment to poison was based on the proud consciousness of possessing a power which enabled her to break through every restraint, to attain every object, to gratify every inclination, to determine the very existence of others.'

This plain, elderly, wizened little woman saw herself as God, with the power of life and death. Zwanziger had led an unsatisfactory, hand-to-mouth existence, profligate in a sordid way, until she discovered the power arsenic gave her. She conceived a veritable frenzy of love for it, calling it her 'truest friend'. She would 'tremble with pleasure as she gazed upon the white powder with eyes beaming with rapture'. In time, says Feuerbach, the mixing and giving of poison became her constant occupation; she practised it in jest and in earnest, and at last with real passion for poison itself, without reference to the object to which it was given.

Jegado was guilty of twenty-six poisonings and eight attempts between the years 1833 and 1851. For all that time this morally diseased servant-maid dealt out death as she chose. Once she had set her heart on any particular victim, she pursued him patiently and remorselessly, and in the majority of cases she murdered without attempting to gain the least advantage for herself. Seven people died in three months in one house where she worked, one of them her own sister. She nursed them all through their protracted agonies with great devotion, and after each death she would say, shaking her head sorrowfully: 'This will not be the last. Wherever I go, people die.' Jegado was very religious and attended Mass regularly.

Van der Linden, between the years 1869 and 1885, attempted the lives of one hundred and two people, of whom twenty-seven died. She was a professional nurse, attentive and kindly, and though she sometimes insured her victims for small sums, she killed mostly simply for the love of killing. Among her victims were her father and mother and three of her own children. To one man who was mourning the sudden death of a relative under her ministrations, she said quietly: 'It will be your turn in a month' – and she duly carried out her prophecy.

Zwanziger, Jegado, and Van der Linden were all small, wizened, and ugly, but they were women in whom lust was intensely strong, and their lust found gratification in the sense of power.

Marie Jeanneret, who was a young and good-looking woman, is an example of a killer who killed for pure love of power. She became a nurse merely to attain this power, and she was actually a loser by most of her crimes. Her psychology is summed up in a phrase she used towards a friend who was condoling with her on the bad luck which attended all her patients: 'Ah, Madame,' said Jeanneret, 'but there are some beautiful moments in death. . . .'

Vacher, who committed many sadistic murders of children, was convinced that he had a sacred mission to punish sinners through the deaths of their offspring. He was a fine-looking, dark-bearded man who, in his white sheepskin cap, had something of the look of an Arab. He had picked up a smattering of education and called himself a 'modern Attila'. He cut girls' throats at the supreme moment of violation, and spoke and wrote of himself after his arrest as 'the instrument of Divine Vengeance'. Vacher, though he falls into Division *B*, had something of the instinct for self-aggrandisement which takes the place of physical frenzy in the murderers of Divison *A*.

Thomas Neill Cream comes undoubtedly both into Division *A* and Division *B*, for, though the sexual impulse and sadism were both concerned in his killings, his driving force was his mania for toying with power.

At the time when he lived and committed his crimes – the year 1892 – he was quite simply considered to have murdered for gain, merely because he wrote fantastic letters to total strangers, demanding huge sums under a threat to blackmail them, after the commission of each murder. There is no evidence that he ever followed up these letters or tried to get into touch with the people to whom he had written them, and it seems that he was merely following his craving for causing talk, and being able to talk himself about the crimes which he had committed, which otherwise would have seemed dull and flat to him. For this is a point which should be carefully noted in connection with murderers of this class. They talk wildly and injudiciously; in many cases, if they could have kept silent they would never have been suspected, but silence is no use to them. They must hear discussions about what they have done, even if they have to start those discussions themselves.

Neill Cream is a very pure example of this class of murderer, and his blackmailing was a clumsy expression of the craving for recognition of the act of killing.

The tale of the Cream killings is a tale of mean streets. In that drab neighbourhood which lies on the south side of the river round about Waterloo lived the murderer and his victims. Stamford Street, Waterloo Road, a place of flat-faced, grimy houses that had seen better days, as their beautiful doorways and fanlights show; Lambeth Road, where the yellow bricks are dark with smoke; Duke Street, a little street of mean lodging-houses; Westminster Bridge Road; and Lambeth Palace Road, whose lordly designation is given the lie by its appearance: these streets formed the theatre for the complicated and sordid drama of a strange lust which was unfolded before the horrified eyes of the nineties. In strange, shabby little rooms, where a normal if a sordid desire was wont to take furtive seekers after 'love' at night, lived the victims of the abnormal doctor with his bald head, his gold watch-chain, his shining silk hat, his crossed eyes behind their gleaming spectacles, and his mellifluous and innocent name of Cream.

Lodging-houses of the baser sort have seen many strange dramas, many curious manifestations of human nature — and that peculiar smell as of many long-past dinners, oilcloth, shut windows, and dusty plush, which greets the nostrils when the door is opened into any of these narrow hallways with their hat-stands and their mottled wall-papers, is perhaps an expression not only of these material causes, but also of that inexpressibly fustian emotion which seems so often to have spent itself within such inauspicious walls.

In *The Times* for 13 April 1892, there was tucked away an inconspicuous little paragraph stating that a police constable had been called into a house in Stamford Street, Waterloo Road, and there in the passage had found a girl, clad only in her night-dress, dying, apparently from the effect of some violent poison. In a room in the same house he found another girl, fully dressed, also apparently suffering in the same way. He took them to St Thomas's Hospital, but Alice Marsh, the first girl, died on the way, Emma Shrivell, the second girl, expiring in great agony some time later. The paragraph went on to state that the two girls were supposed to have been poisoned by some tinned salmon they had taken a few hours earlier.

An inquest was held at St Thomas's Hospital by Mr Wyatt, the Day-Coroner for East Surrey. Constable Eversfield described how he had been fetched to the Stamford Street house and in what condition he had found Alice Marsh and Emma Shrivell, and how Shrivell had told him that a 'gentleman' had given each of them some 'long pills', after which he had accompanied them home and stayed there until two o'clock in the morning. After he had left, they ate some tinned fish which had made them extremely ill. She said that she had met this gentleman before, the only name she knew him by was Fred, and that he was very bald on the top of his head and wore spectacles and a silk hat.

The next witness was Inspector Lowe, who stated that he went to the house in Stamford Street and found a letter there from some man, accepting an invitation to tea from the two girls. The house physician at St Thomas's stated that Shrivell was already unconscious when she arrived at the hospital and suffering from attacks of convulsions. She was kept under the influence of chloroform for some time; directly it was taken from her she died. He had made a post-mortem on the bodies of both girls, but found no sign of disease, and considered the symptoms were not consistent with ptomaine poisoning. In his opinion strychnine had been the cause of death. The inquiry was adjourned for an analysis to be made of the contents of the stomachs.

On Friday, 6 May, the inquest was resumed, but no further evidence was forthcoming until Mr Thomas Stephenson, Government analyst, was called. He stated that he had found traces of strychnine, and the jury returned a verdict that death in each case was due to strychnine poisoning, but that how it had been administered there was no evidence to show.

Here the question of these deaths might have rested for ever had it not been for the conduct of the murderer. On 13 October of the previous year a girl called Ellen Donworth, of the class so justly termed 'unfortunate', had been brought into St Thomas's Hospital dead. But before she had gone out on the evening that she met her death Ellen had told a friend that she was going to meet a gentleman outside the York Hotel in the Waterloo Road, and that she had to give back to him the letter she had received from him making the appointment. She mentioned that this man was bald-headed and cross-eyed. An hour and a half later she was brought back dying by two men who had found her in the street. She gasped out that the man who had written the letter – the 'tall, dark, cross-eyed fellow' – had given her some white stuff to drink out of a bottle. She died in great agony, and the symptoms were consistent with strychnine poisoning.

The house surgeon made an analysis of the contents of the stomach and found some strychnine, about a quarter of a grain of which was unabsorbed. An inquest was held, but the police were without any clue, and Ellen Donworth was buried without having become a *cause célèbre*. On the 20th of the same month died a girl called Matilda Clover, a single

143

woman with a child who lived at 27 Lambeth Road. Unlike Alice Marsh and Emma Shrivell, she had caused no undue comment by her death, and a careless doctor's assistant, who did not even see her die, obtained from his employer a certificate stating that the cause of death was delirium tremens and syncope. Clover, a lonely, friendless creature, was buried and her baby taken to the workhouse; her name would soon have passed from the memory even of those who had known her had it not been for a very peculiar circumstance. Sir William Broadbent, a well-known physician, received the following letter:

London, 28 November, 1891

Sir,

Miss Clover, who until a short time ago lived at 27, Lambeth Road, S.E., died at the above address on October 20 (last month) through being poisoned with strychnine. After her death a search of her effects was made, and evidence was found which showed that you not only gave her the medicine which caused her death, but that you had been hired for the purpose of poisoning her. The evidence is in the hands of one of our detectives, who will give the evidence either to you or to the police authorities for the sum of £2500 (Two thousand five hundred pounds sterling).[1] You can have the evidence for £2500, and in that way save yourself from ruin. If the matter is disposed of to the police, it will be made public by being published in the papers, and ruin you for ever. You know well enough that an accusation of that sort will ruin you for ever. Now, sir, if you want the evidence for £2500, just put a personal in the *Daily Chronicle*, saying you will pay Malone £2500 for his services, and I will send a party to settle the matter. If you do not want the evidence, of course, it will be turned over to the police at once and published, and your ruin will surely follow. Think well before you decide on this matter. It is just this, £2500 sterling on the one hand, and ruin, shame, and disgrace on the other. Answer by personal on the first page of the *Daily Chronicle* any time next week.

1. EDITOR'S NOTE: The 1991 purchasing power of the 1891 pound is about £35.50.

I am not humbugging you. I have evidence strong enough to ruin you for ever.

M. MALONE

Sir William Broadbent sent the letter to Scotland Yard, where it was pigeon-holed and forgotten.

Mr Frederick Smith, a member of the firm of W.H. Smith and Son, had also been the recipient of a peculiar letter, in his case signed 'Bayne'. This letter was as follows:

London, 5 November, 1891

Sir,

On Tuesday night, 13 October (last month) a girl named Ellen Donworth, but sometimes called Ellen Linnell [Ellen Donworth was living with a man called Linnell] who lived at 8 Duke Street, Westminster Bridge Road, was poisoned by strychnine. After her death among her effects were found two letters criminating you, which if they ever became public property will surely convict you of the crime. I enclose you a copy of one of the letters which the girl received on the morning of 13 October (the day on which she died). Just read it and then judge for yourself what hope you have of escape if the law officers ever get hold of these letters. Think of the shame and disgrace it will bring on your family if you are arrested and put in prison for this crime. My object in writing to you is to ask if you will retain me at once as your counsellor and legal adviser. If you employ me at once to act for you in the matter, I will save you from all exposure and shame in the matter, but if you wait until arrested before retaining me, then I cannot act for you, as no lawyer can save you after the authorities get hold of these two letters. If you wish to retain me, just write a few lines on a paper saying – 'Mr Fred Smith wishes to see Mr Bayne, the barrister, at once.' Paste this in one of your shop windows at 186 Strand next Tuesday morning, and when I see it I will drop in and have a private interview with you. I can save you if you retain me in time, but not otherwise.

Yours truly,

H. BAYNE

The enclosed letter referred to was as follows:

Miss Ellen Linnell,
I wrote and warned you at once before that Frederick Smith, of W.H. Smith & Son, was going to poison you, and I am writing now to say that if you take any of the medicine he gave you you will die. I saw Frederick Smith prepare the medicine he gave you, and I saw him put enough strychnine in the medicine for to kill a horse. If you take any of it you will die.

H.M.B.

A personage calling himself A. O'Brien, detective, had previously written to the Coroner during the inquest on Donworth, offering for the modest sum of £300,000 to bring her murderer to justice. It afterwards transpired that O'Brien and Bayne were one and the same, and that neither was the true name of the writer. This letter, like the letter to Sir William Broadbent, was pigeon-holed at Scotland Yard, and Donworth and Clover rested untroubled in their graves. But it is worth mentioning that Ellen Donworth had actually received on the morning of 13 October, the last morning she was ever to see, the letter a copy of which H. Bayne enclosed to Mr Smith.

Six months had passed between the deaths of Clover and Donworth and those of Marsh and Shrivell, and even as Sir William Broadbent and Mr Smith had received letters after the first two tragedies, so a Dr Harper of Barnstaple received a very similar epistle after Marsh and Shrivell died. This letter ran as follows:

London, 25 April, 1892

Dear Sir,
I am writing to inform you that one of my operators has indisputable evidence that your son, W. H. Harper, a medical student at St Thomas's Hospital, poisoned two girls, named Alice Marsh and Emma Shrivell, on the 12th inst., and that I am willing to give you the said evidence, that you may suppress it, for £1500 sterling, or sell it to the police for the same amount. The publication of the

evidence would ruin you and your family for ever, and you know it as well as I do. To show you what I am writing is true, I am willing to send you a copy of the evidence against your son, so that you may read it. You will need no one to tell you that it will convict your son. Answer my letter at once through the columns of the London *Daily Chronicle*, as follows:

'W.H.M. ... Will pay you for your services. – Dr H.' When I see this in the paper I will communicate with you again. As I said before, I am perfectly willing to satisfy you that I have strong evidence against your son. If you don't answer it I am going to give evidence to the Coroner at once.

Yours truly,

W. H. MURRAY

Enclosed with this letter were not only several newspaper cuttings relating to the deaths of Marsh and Shrivell, but also the following printed slip:

Ellen Donworth's death. To the guests of the Metropole Hotel. I hereby certify you that the person who poisoned Ellen Donworth on the 13th day of last October is today in the employ of the Metropole Hotel, and your lives are in danger as long as you remain in this hotel.

W. H. MURRAY

Dr Harper had a son who was a student at St Thomas's Hospital and who lodged in the Lambeth Palace Road, and at the same house there lodged a man calling himself Thomas Neill. Dr Harper wrote at once to his son, and they agreed to consult Scotland Yard. There were by now several of the Murray letters – one to Dr Harper, another to Coroner Wyatt and the foreman of the jury, who sat upon the bodies of Marsh and Shrivell, and the third to a Mr Clark, a private inquiry agent at Cockspur Street – all accusing young Harper of having poisoned the girls.

It is important to notice that in the case of Clover, whose death was brought in as being from delirium tremens, no one except her murderer could have known that she had died of poisoning, and therefore the man, whoever it was, who had written the letter to Sir William Broadbent must have been the man who was guilty of her death, for it was dated 28 November 1891. The only point in which the writer of the letter was incorrect was that he stated Clover had died on 20 October, whereas as a matter of fact she did not expire until 21 October, but this was a natural mistake to be made by the man who had himself administered the poison on the earlier date. But about that same date in October, Dr Cream told his landlady's daughter, Miss Sleaper, that a friend of his, a young lady with a child, had been poisoned in Lambeth Road, and suggested that Miss Sleaper should go round and make inquiries as to whether she were dead or not. This, Miss Sleaper, not liking the errand, refused to do. Dr Neill, as he was then called, further informed Miss Sleaper that he knew who had poisoned the girl in Lambeth Road: he said that it was Lord Russell. The Russell matrimonial suit was then being heard, and Lady Russell was the recipient of a letter very similar to those that had been received by Sir William Broadbent and Mr Smith. Countess Russell received this letter in the December of 1891, and showed it to various people, including Mr George Lewis, the solicitor, but then proceeded to lose the letter, and therefore it did not go to swell the curious little collection at Scotland Yard. Miss Sleaper appears to have had all the qualifications of a confidante, for her lodger also informed her that he was engaged to be married, and showed her the portrait of his fiancée – Miss Laura Sabatini. All this was in the latter end of 1891.

In January of 1892 the doctor went to Canada, previously making a will, as was only right and prudent, in favour of Miss Sabatini. He returned to Lambeth Palace Road on Saturday, 9 April, and on 17 April, the Sunday after the deaths of Marsh and Shrivell, when the report of the first inquiries was in the papers, he discussed their deaths with his usual confidante, Emily Sleaper, who seems always to have been made vaguely uneasy by the insistence with which he would persist in thrusting his opinions upon her. On this occasion he told her the two girls had been murdered in cold blood, though, as a matter of fact, strychnine had not yet been found, the only mention of foul play being the opinion of the St Thomas's house physician. About three weeks later he told her that her other lodger, Mr Harper, was the guilty man, a statement the truth of which Miss Sleaper denied with much indignation. Cream even made an opportunity to go into Mr Harper's room on the drawing-room floor, and when Miss Sleaper found him there, asked her questions about her other lodger and looked through that gentleman's medical books.

Neill Cream had to talk — that was the whole matter; without speech his secret could give him no satisfaction, and he confided his opinions to an acquaintance of his, a young man called Haynes, who lodged at the house of a Mr and Mrs Armstead in the Westminster Bridge Road. Mr Armstead was a photographer, and Neill Cream went to his house several times to have his photograph taken, another curious desire for the enhancement of personality which it might be thought a murderer would be prudent enough to resist. Neill Cream opened the subject of the deaths of Marsh and Shrivell with young Haynes in the month of May. Cream stated that Walter Harper, his fellow-lodger, was the guilty man, and that he had not only poisoned Marsh and Shrivell, but three other women as well — Ellen Donworth, Matilda Clover, and Lou Harvey. Not content with having brought up this array of names, Cream insisted on dragging Haynes with him in a weird pilgrimage to the house in Lambeth Road where Matilda Clover had died. He insisted that Haynes should go into the house, while he himself waited outside, and inquire if Matilda Clover had died there from poisoning. He then dragged Mr Haynes on all the way to Townsend Road, St John's Wood, where Lou Harvey had resided. This Lou Harvey, so Cream informed Haynes, had been poisoned by Harper at a music-hall and must have fallen dead either there or between it and another music-hall. He gave the names of these two places of entertainment as the Royal and the Oxford.

Mr Haynes was obscurely troubled by the strange, excited manner of his informant, yet his statement seemed so circumstantial — for Cream even went to the length of declaring that Harper had told him that he was in great trouble and asked him for some strychnine — that he felt something ought to be done about the matter, and therefore he repaired to Scotland Yard. Haynes had at one time followed the profession of private inquiry agent, being, indeed, a secret agent sometimes employed by the Home Office, and when Cream found this out he became more confidential than ever. He showed Haynes the photograph of young Harper which he had stolen from Miss Sleaper's album. Armed with what he considered first-hand knowledge, Mr Haynes saw Detective Sergeant M'Intyre, whom he had known for some years, suppressing, however, the name of Neill Cream according to a promise he had made. M'Intyre made inquiries at the house in Townsend Road, but could find out nothing about Lou Harvey, who seemed to have disappeared into space. The only thing certain about her, and that was negative, was that no one of that name had been reported to Scotland Yard as having died in suspicious circumstances. The inquiry dragged on and died a natural death. Then there came the day when Dr Harper of Barnstaple received the letter signed W. H. Murray, and this letter he sent to Scotland Yard, where, by a fateful coincidence, it was given to Detective M'Intyre, who already possessed that other letter signed Murray which had been sent to the jury at the inquest on Marsh and Shrivell, as well as the letter which had been addressed to Sir William Broadbent, and signed Malone.

The police knew, of course, that Marsh and Shrivell had been poisoned, but Lou Harvey they had failed to trace; the bodies of Clover and Donworth were now exhumed, and the result of an analysis proved that these two also had been poisoned with strychnine. The only clues connecting these cases, excepting the similarity of the poison, were the letters, which were signed in different names and were in two different writings.

Meanwhile, the one remaining thing needful to wreck him utterly had been done by Neill Cream: not content with brandishing the word 'murder' before murder had ever been thought of in connection with the names he mentioned, not content with writing his childish letters and dragging his acquaintances about to houses with which otherwise he himself would never have been connected, he claimed the protection of the police. He saw Detective M'Intyre, whom he already knew slightly as a friend of the Armsteads, who had introduced him earlier in the month, described himself as a commercial traveller and complained of being followed. He asked that M'Intyre should look into the matter and save him from this annoyance in future. M'Intyre had no cause at this time to suspect Cream of murder, but something strange about the man made him decide to make inquiries about him.

It was not without reason that Cream complained to Detective Sergeant M'Intyre that he was being watched. On the fateful morning of 12 April, Police Constable Comley had been passing along Stamford Street when he saw a man come out of Number 118; the light of a street-lamp which was directly opposite the door fell upon the man's face: he was about five feet ten inches, apparently between forty and fifty years of age, wore a high silk hat and glasses; he had a moustache, but no whiskers. This was at about 1.45 am. George Comley noticed also the young woman who let the man out; she was Emma Shrivell, whom he was to see an hour later being carried to a cab by Eversfield in her death agonies. Comley himself, when he came upon that tragic scene, carried Marsh into the cab and went with both girls and Eversfield to the hospital. He questioned Shrivell as to what she had eaten, and, according to him, she replied: 'I have had some supper, and a gentleman gave us three pills each.' Comley asked her: 'Was it the gentleman you let out at a quarter to two, with glasses on?' and she replied: 'Yes.'

At the time when Comley had observed the man being let out he did not think much of the circumstances, for, as he afterwards said in cross-examination: 'At that time of night a number of men came from such houses.' What a picture, in that simple and commonplace sentence, of furtive seekers after passion going their way homeward from the sordid houses which had harboured them for an hour or so!

This morning of 12 April was cold and dark, and the man walked briskly away, but Police Constable Comley had obtained a good view of him and duly described him in his report. A month later, in Westminster Bridge Road, Police Constable Comley felt certain he saw him again. The man, of whose identity he was still ignorant, was loitering up and down watching the women that passed, scrutinising the prostitutes closely. Presently he went off with a woman to her room in Elliott's Row, and was with her there for an hour and a half, while Comley and Ward — the latter a Police Sergeant who had been furnished with the description of the man seen coming out of the Stamford Street house — were watching for him outside. Later the suspected man let himself into 103 Lambeth Palace Road with a latch-key. Since this occurrence, the house in Lambeth Palace Road had been under observation, Cream himself had been followed, and the Armstead house was watched whenever he was there. Indeed, one day when Cream was at their house, Mrs Armstead drew his attention and that of her husband to the fact that observation was being kept upon them, whereupon Cream pointed to a man standing in the roadway and asked if that were one of the watchers, adding, entirely out of the blue: 'What a dreadful murder that was in Stamford Street!' Mrs Armstead asked him whether he had known the two girls, and he replied that he knew them very well indeed; he had often seen them up on the Bridge, where they used to solicit. Mr Armstead made inquiries and found out that it was Neill Cream who was being watched. The next day he asked him why he was followed and why he had not told him. Cream replied that he had intended to tell him later that the police were mistaking him for Mr Harper, who lived in the same house.

After Cream complained about being followed, M'Intyre began inquiries about him and discovered that Comley had declared him to be like the man whom he had seen leave the Stamford Street house. M'Intyre continued to keep up with Cream, and on one occasion went with him into 'The Pheasant' public house with Inspector Harvey and Chief-Inspector Mulvaney. Cream complained that a few nights earlier he had met a woman of the unfortunate class, whom he termed 'a rip', in the Westminster Bridge Road and that she told him she had been set to spy on him by the police. M'Intyre suggested that Cream should fetch his letters and his case of samples to prove that he really was the commercial traveller he gave himself out as being, a proposition to which Cream eagerly assented. It is noteworthy that when M'Intyre in the first place asked him why he thought he was being shadowed, Cream had replied he thought it was because he had some indecent photographs in his possession and went about a lot with loose women. The net was now almost ready to close round Neill Cream, but the authorities wished to have absolutely unassailable evidence before they struck. The paper on which the letter to Dr Harper had been written bore the watermark — 'Fairfield Superfine Quality' — of a mill in Canada, the country where Cream had so lately been. M'Intyre got Cream to write him a sentence or two on a sheet of notepaper at the latter's lodgings and found the same watermark.

Cream now began to be seriously disturbed about his acquaintance with the detective — an acquaintance which he himself had started. It will be seen to what incredible lengths Cream went in his foolishness when it is known that during his acquaintance with M'Intyre he had spun him a story about a man called Murray (it will be remembered that some of the blackmailing letters were signed 'Murray') by whom he said he had been stopped in the street about a week before the last inquest on Marsh and Shrivell. This phantom man Murray had, according to Cream, questioned him about young Harper and showed him a letter addressed to Shrivell and Marsh warning them to be careful of Dr Harper, as he would serve them as he had done the girls Clover and Harvey. Murray, according to Cream, was a detective in charge of the case. Up to the moment when Cream invented this story for the benefit of M'Intyre, the latter had not heard the names of Clover and Harvey. Cream even described the mythical Murray as being a man of about forty years of age, five feet nine inches high, and wearing a dark beard, whiskers, and moustache. Cream's nervous restlessness of temperament drove him from revelation to revelation and invention to invention; sometimes he would be taken with fits of trembling, sometimes he would be apparently light-hearted and carefree.

However, by 26 May he had become thoroughly nervous and, on meeting M'Intyre in Westminster Bridge Road, committed the imprudence of telling him that he wanted to go away and asking him whether he was likely to be arrested if he attempted to leave London. M'Intyre replied that he could not tell, but advised him to go along with him to Scotland Yard and find out if they had anything against him. They had walked some distance over the bridge when Cream suddenly stopped and told M'Intyre he suspected he was not playing straight with him; he even went to the fantastic lengths of saying he would consult a solicitor about being annoyed in this way by the police and asked M'Intyre to recommend him one. The detective pointed out that this would hardly be consistent with his position and the two men parted.

On 3 June, authority moved and Cream was arrested at his rooms, though he was charged not with murder, but with attempt to extort money from Dr Harper of Barnstaple by means of false pretences. All Cream said when arrested was: 'You have got the wrong man; fire away!' The inspector who made the arrest — Inspector Tonbridge — showed him the envelope in which the letter had been sent to Dr Harper, saying: 'This is what you are accused of sending.' Cream replied: 'That is not my writing.' Tonbridge took the letter out of the envelope and said: 'This is the letter,' to which Cream made no reply. On Tuesday, 12 July, after having been several times remanded on the original charge and being in court in the custody of two warders when the inquest was held on the exhumed body of Matilda Clover, Cream was brought up at Bow Street and charged with the wilful murder of Matilda Clover.

A dramatic turn was given to these proceedings by the appearance in the living flesh of Lou Harvey, who had been so much more fortunate than those other sister professionals. Her real name was Harris, but after the fashion of these women, she had taken temporarily the name of the man with whom she was living — a good-for-nothing young house-painter called Charles Harvey. She told how, in the October of the previous year, she had been spoken to by a man whom she now recognised as Cream outside St James's Hall. As usual, Cream had felt that he must satisfy both his lusts as nearly together as possible, and he spent that night with her at a hotel in Berwick Street; and in the morning, when leaving her, made an appointment to meet her again that evening on the Embankment, when, he said, he would give her some pills to cure some spots which he had noticed on her forehead. She met him that evening and he told her he had brought the pills and that she had better have a glass of wine first; he took her with him to the Northumberland public house and gave her wine, and also some roses — strangely beautiful and poetic gifts to come from such a man.

They left the public house and walked back towards the Embankment, and it was then he produced the pills, after telling her he would not be able to go with her to a music-hall as arranged, but that she was to go, and he would meet her at eleven o'clock and take her to the same hotel as the previous night. There was probably in his mind a sense of excitement and pleasure at the thought of her sitting in the music-hall, where, as he thought, she would be taken with the pains of death. He gave her the pills — the 'long pills' that the other women described — and told her to swallow them whole. Some instinct warned Lou Harvey of danger, and, while pretending to swallow them, she really passed them into her other hand. He asked her to show him her right hand, into which he had put the pills, and she did so, which satisfied him; meanwhile she had dropped the pills unobserved into the roadway. He gave her five shillings to pay for her seat at the music-hall and wanted to put her into a cab, doubtless so that he should be sure of her going there, but she told him she would find a cab for herself. She was really meaning to meet Harvey, who, unknown to Cream, had accompanied her that evening. Harvey seems to have been a most ignoble person, who never worked unless he could not avoid it, and who said it was nothing to do with him what Louisa did for a living. Nevertheless he too felt there was something suspicious about this offer of medicine from a strange man, and he had accompanied her that evening to see that all was well. He and Lou went away together, and for once Neill Cream was cheated of his sensation. How this rankled may be guessed from the inquiries that he perpetually made in his desire to find out how and where she had died.

The long, fantastic dance was over at last. After his successful murders of Donworth and Clover, Cream had become engaged to Miss Sabatini, had gone for a trip to Canada, and then come back again to his old haunts, compelled by Heaven only knows what desire and inward compulsion, and there this strange lust for power had claimed gratification once more, and Marsh and Shrivell had died as successfully as Clover and Donworth, in long-drawn-out agonies; and Cream had had the satisfaction of reading the account of their sufferings in the daily papers.

Still with that inward compulsion strong upon him, he had had to keep on and on at the subject with everyone he knew, careering round London with the puzzled Haynes, pestering Scotland Yard, pumping Miss Sleaper about his harmless fellow-lodger, and all the while pursuing his dirty amours with this and that woman whom he picked up at the street-corners known to him. Doubtless, if his own fantastic piping had not drawn attention to the strangeness of his measure these other women, too, in their turn would have danced the dance of death at his bidding. With each success his satisfaction at the power he carried had increased, until he felt that he must hear discussion about the thing at whatever cost. That he was a fearful and timorous man there is no doubt, in spite of his incredible rashness. He was terrified of arrest, always subject to nervous tremblings, restless and uneasy even when no one suspected him, bold to rashness when they did. It is impossible to say what sort of emotion went on in that hardly human mind when it realised that the game was up at last, that the fantastic dance across an ocean and round about mean streets was ended.

In the dock Neill Cream appeared composed and pleaded 'Not Guilty' to the charge of the wilful murder of Alice Marsh, Ellen Donworth, Emma Shrivell, and Matilda Clover, also to the charges of sending Joseph Harper a letter demanding money with menaces, of sending a similar letter to William Henry Broadbent, and of attempting to administer to Louisa Harvey a large quantity of strychnine to murder her.

The Attorney-General, Sir Charles Russell — afterwards Lord Russell of Killowen and Lord Chief Justice — conducted the prosecution; Mr Geoghegan led for the defence. The trial lasted from Tuesday, 18 October, to Saturday the 22nd, and gradually there was piled up by witness after witness a terrible picture of the life that Cream and his victims had lived. From a baptismal certificate found among Cream's papers, he appeared to have been born in May 1850. His father was a Scotsman and lived in Glasgow, but had emigrated when his son Thomas was a child to America. There Neill Cream seems to have received a medical education and possessed some kind of a degree, and a Mr Levy, a licensed victualler, was called to prove that Cream was practising in Chicago as a physician in 1881. Cream arrived in England on 1 October 1891, and came to Anderton's Hotel in London; while there, on 6 October, he met in the street a young woman called Eliza Masters. With her he went to Gatti's music-hall, where she introduced him to a friend called Elizabeth May. Both these women were of that class never more truly dubbed 'unfortunate' than in this particular case, and had some curious evidence to give. They lived in the inappropriately named Orient Buildings off the Lambeth Road. The kindly fate that was to protect Lou Harvey was watching over these two also, for there can be little doubt that Cream had marked them down for his first victims in London. On 9 October Eliza Masters received a letter stating that the writer would come and see her between three and five o'clock that afternoon. He recalled himself to her by mentioning the evening at Gatti's music-hall, and he made the curious request, which he made at other times to other women — namely, that she was not to destroy the letter as he wished to get it back when he came to see her. Masters and May were of the kind that hunt in couples, and accordingly Masters told her friend of the expected visitor and the two women were on the look-out together when the hour arrived.

As they sat looking out of the window, they saw coming along on the opposite side of the street a young woman whom they knew by sight but not by name; she was carrying a basket and she wore, as was her custom, a white apron with straps that crossed over her shoulders. After her down the street, trailing her as a wild animal might trail its prey, came their expected visitor. The young woman looked round once or twice, as though fully recognising that she was being followed, and once she smiled — probably her professional smile. Not turning into Orient Buildings as he should have done to keep his appointment, the man kept on after her. Excited — perhaps annoyed at what they may have considered a breach of professional etiquette on the part of this young woman poaching, so to speak, upon their preserves — May and Masters went down into the street and in their turn followed the other two. They saw the girl go to the door of Number 27 Lambeth Road and wait until the man came up with her; the girl opened the door, the two went in, and it was shut behind them. The baffled Eliza and her friend waited for half-an-hour, but the man did not come out again during that time, and Masters never saw him again until she was asked to go to Bow Street to identify him.

Between the date when Neill Cream met Matilda Clover and the date on which she died occurred the tragedy of Ellen Donworth. She had been picked up in the street on 13 October between six and seven o'clock in the evening; she was in great agony and, like Alice Marsh, died on the way to St Thomas's Hospital in a cab. There was not sufficient evidence to connect anyone with her death, and yet on 19 October it was proved that Cream had written to the Deputy Coroner a letter, to which reference has already been made, offering to bring the murderer of Ellen Donworth to justice for the fee of three hundred thousand pounds. On 5 November he wrote the letter to Mr Smith, in which he enclosed a copy of the note he had sent to Ellen Donworth, or Linnell. Comparison of the dates of this period will show a most strange and hardly credible series of facts. On the night of 20 October, or the morning of the 21st, he met Lou Harvey, spent the night at Berwick Street Hotel with her, and the next evening attempted to murder her. It seems as though Cream must have suffered from attacks of his mania which worked him up to such a terrific pitch that one indulgence only made him crave another immediately before he felt his desires slaked.

Cream comes to London on 5 October, meets Masters and May on the 6th, arranges to meet them again on the 9th – the time in the meanwhile having been occupied by finding himself the lodgings in the Lambeth Palace Road – forgets about them and does, indeed, meet Matilda Clover; on 13 October poisons Ellen Donworth; on the 20th kills Clover; and on the 22nd endeavours to kill Lou Harvey. Small wonder that after this he was content to let the field of his dreadful passions lie fallow for a while, contenting himself with perpetually dragging the fact of the deaths up in conversation and letters. When Inspector Tonbridge searched Cream's bedroom after his arrest he found an envelope on which the following was written: '19 October, M.C. 13 October — 11 April, E.S. 23 October, L.H.' Still, in spite of his foolish behaviour, there is no doubt that if Neill Cream had chosen not to return from Canada in April of the following year he could have gone to his grave in the full course of time, free from any accusation regarding the deaths of Clover and Donworth.

Gradually the household at 27 Lambeth Road was presented before the jury. The landlady of the house, a Mrs Voules or Phillips, seems to have been instrumental in hushing up the death as much as possible, doubtless not wishing her rooms to obtain an unenviable notoriety. Mrs Voules had carried her desire for pleasantness to such a point that when she registered the death she stated that Clover had been a charwoman, and that she had been present at her death, which was not the case; her rather feeble excuse to Mr Justice Hawkins was that she had made that statement from want of thought. The servant-girl at 27 Lambeth Road was called Lucy Rose. Clover had two rooms on the top floor and had living with her her little boy. On the day before Clover died, Lucy Rose found in her room an open letter lying beside its envelope. After the habit of servant-maids, Lucy Rose read the letter; it was an invitation asking Matilda Clover to meet the writer, who signed himself 'Fred', outside Canterbury Hall at seven-thirty that evening. In the letter was an injunction that Matilda Clover should bring it with her when she was keeping the appointment, and the envelope also. After Clover's death, Lucy Rose hunted everywhere for the letter, but failed to find it. Before going out, apparently to keep the appointment, Clover asked Lucy Rose to help her put her child to bed, which the girl did, and at about seven-thirty Clover went out. Later, probably about nine o'clock, she came back and was let in by Lucy; she had with her a man who, as well as Lucy could see by the light of the small paraffin lamp, was tall and broad and had a heavy moustache; he was wearing a large coat with a cape to it and a silk hat. This apparently commonplace meeting in the lodging-house hall between these three people with the exquisite pastoral names of Rose, Clover and Cream — which might well be a refrain from lyric poetry — would have been curious indeed to anyone who could have seen through outward appearances and into the people's minds. Lucy Rose — a little lodging-house drudge, but kind-hearted, willing to help put the baby to bed in spite of the heaviness of her own work — little knew when she would see that apparently ordinary client of Matilda Clover again. Poor Clover — the girl who had smiled over her shoulder at this same man eleven days earlier — was probably prepared to go through with the usual routine without any special emotions on the subject, unconscious of the fact that her span of life was already as good as ended. And Cream himself, standing there in his big overcoat and his silk hat, with the poison in his pocket — who can say what exultant thoughts, what a rising tide of excitement, were welling within him?

Once more Clover went out, to fetch some beer, and later still Lucy Rose heard a door open — Clover apparently letting the man out of the house, as she heard some words of good-night spoken between them. About an hour later still Clover again went out, and had not returned before Lucy Rose went to sleep. Rose was awakened at about three o'clock by the sound of screaming. She called the landlady and they went into Clover's room. They found her in great agony lying across the bed, her head wedged between the side of the bed and the wall. She declared that she had been poisoned; she twitched violently, vomited, and had violent convulsions. Mrs Voules sent for a Dr Graham, but his assistant — a man named Coppin — arrived in his stead. Coppin received the impression that Clover suffered from epileptic fits and alcoholic poisoning, and the landlady told him she was in the habit of drinking too much. He was only with her about ten or twelve minutes. He sent her some medicine to stop the vomiting; but he thought that she was dying, and gave it to Dr Graham as his opinion that drink was the

161

cause. Mrs Voules sent again for Coppin, but he did not come. Clover grew steadily worse, and all through her hours of agony the little servant-girl sat with her — once making her a cup of tea and once giving her some soda and milk. In the moments of relief between the spasms she was calm and collected and asked to see her baby. She did not die till nine o'clock in the morning. Dr Graham next day gave a certificate of death from the information that Mrs Voules and Mr Coppin had given him — a proceeding that the Attorney-General stigmatised as a grave dereliction of duty. Matilda Clover was buried in a pauper's grave, her child was taken to the workhouse, and her new boots were pawned by Mrs Voules. Not a soul suspected that Matilda Clover had been murdered, and yet Cream spoke of such a possibility to Miss Sleaper and wrote the letter signed 'Malone' to Sir William Broadbent.

It is a curious point that the man with whom Matilda Clover had been living, and who was the father of her child, was called Fred — a small, slight, fair man with blue eyes. They had quarrelled seriously, and he had taken himself off, much to Clover's grief, about a month before she met Cream; but, if Lucy Rose's memory was to be trusted, the letter she had found on the table making an appointment with Clover was signed Fred, and it will be remembered that Marsh and Shrivell knew Neill Cream only as Fred. There was no shadow of suspicion against the real, original Fred, and it seems likely that Cream had told Clover, on hearing her story, that he also was called Fred, and had stuck to the name when starting on his second series of murders. Perhaps he thought to incriminate — should any question arise about Clover's death — her previous lover; perhaps he was merely adopting the first name that came into his head, as he would naturally not wish to give his own. Be that as it may, Lucy Rose, at one of her examinations, insisted that Clover had gasped out that she was poisoned and that that 'wretch Fred' had done it; although Mrs Voules, consistent in her desire to thwart any suggestion of foul play, had stoutly denied that Clover had said anything of the kind. Mr Coppin declared that no mention of poison was made to him, and thus it came about that even his adoption of the name of Clover's lover was not necessary to Cream as a protection. The question of poison was never raised at all except by Cream's own letters and statements.

A commercial traveller called John Wilson M'Culloch was able to throw light upon Cream's life in Canada. The two men had met in the February of 1892 at Blanchard's Hotel in Quebec. M'Culloch was not introduced to Cream, but merely fell into the habit of conversing with him as one hotel acquaintance does with another. Cream called him into his room and showed him samples of pills and about eighteen or twenty bottles of various sizes. Out of a cash-box he produced another bottle — about three inches long — and asked M'Culloch if he knew what was in it. M'Culloch replying in the negative, Cream said: 'That's poison.' 'For God's sake, what do you want that for?' asked the startled M'Culloch, to which Cream replied: 'I give that to women to get them out of the family way; I give it to them in these,' and he showed M'Culloch some capsules. It may well be that the promise of bringing about abortion or of preventing conception was the inducement that Cream used to make the women take his pills. Cream talked a lot to M'Culloch about London and told him that he had 'lots of fun with women' there. He mentioned Waterloo, Victoria, and Westminster Bridge Road as his hunting grounds.

Cream had all the insensate egoism of the born criminal, and he dragged M'Culloch about Quebec, showing him where his brother and other relations had lived and been in business and where he himself had worked as a boy. He showed him a photograph of Miss Sabatini and photographs of other women. He had shown Masters and May photographs of himself and of his mother on the occasion of his meeting them in the music-hall; and, indeed, showing people photographs of himself or of anything to do with him seems to have been a favourite occupation of his. M'Culloch grew to dislike his hotel acquaintance, who had, as he said, 'a loose tongue about women,' and who showed him indecent photographs as well as the family portraits. Cream confided to him also that he practised abortion, and showed him a pair of false whiskers and a beard which, he said, he wore when operating to prevent identification.

The usual evidence as to the possession of poison was gone into. A chemist gave evidence that Cream had bought nux vomica from him, and also gelatine capsules, which he had changed the next day for a smaller size. Dr Stevenson, the Home Office analyst, had received from Inspector Tonbridge a case found in Cream's room containing fifty-four bottles of pills and several boxes of coated pills. Of the fifty-four bottles, seven contained strychnine — each pill containing strychnine in medicinal quantity — one twenty-second of a grain to each pill : twenty-two of them would make a complete grain and eleven of them half a grain, rather less than half a grain being a fatal dose. The general nature of the pills was sugary and sticky, and from four to twenty could be got into each capsule according to its size, but if strychnine crystals alone were put into the capsule it would hold more of the poison. It was admitted by the prosecution that Cream himself was in the habit of occasionally taking strychnine, and he also drugged himself frequently with morphia and opium, and had done so for years.

The most pathetic figure during the trial was that of Laura Sabatini — a respectable girl who had worked as a dressmaker and lived with her mother at Berkhampstead. She had to confess that she had written some of the letters herself at Cream's dictation, and this accounted for a fact that had puzzled Scotland Yard — the fact that all the letters were not in the same writing and that only some of them corresponded to the specimen they had obtained of Cream's hand. Miss Sabatini had written the letter to Coroner Wyatt enclosing a note to the jury — both signed 'Murray'; also the letter to Clark, the private detective. She had asked Cream why he used the name Murray, and he said it was a friend of his, a detective, who was examining into the case and that some day he would tell her all about it. She became engaged to Cream in 1891, and in January 1892 he went to America for the purpose, so he said, of seeing about his father's estate. Before his departure he made a will in her favour in which he described himself as Thomas Neill Cream, physician, late of the city of Quebec, and left her the whole of his property. This will was in the same handwriting as the blackmailing letters. It was obvious that, though puzzled, Laura Sabatini had written the other letters in good faith, for, although she realised that they made a terrible accusation against Harper, she thought that Cream with his friend Murray was at work upon the case. The first that she knew of his being in danger was when he was actually arrested.

Mr Geoghegan's speech for the defence was a brilliant exposition of the gentle art of making bricks without straw. He made the most of the fact that Lucy Rose had not recognised the prisoner when she was taken to identify him, and that her description of a man with a heavy moustache and silk hat might apply to forty thousand respectable people walking about the streets of London; that Matilda Clover had lived for an extraordinarily long time after the dose of strychnine if it had been administered to her by the man in question; and that accurate identification by May and Masters of a man whom they had only seen once and whom they were looking down upon from a window high up was unlikely. But the array of facts was overwhelming, and Mr Justice Hawkins in his summing-up left no doubt as to which way he expected the jury to decide. The jury was only absent for twelve minutes and returned a verdict of Wilful Murder. The prisoner made no answer when asked if he had anything to say as to why the court should not give him judgment to die according to the law: and Mr Justice Hawkins accordingly passed sentence of death. Cream listened intently, but betrayed no emotion, and was removed quietly from the dock and the sight of the world of men and women.

It is almost certain that nowadays Neill Cream would

have been found insane, but in the leading article of *The Times* for 22 October 1892 there was a certain note of smug satisfaction that Cream was to die:

> Nobody who has read the evidence can doubt the justice of his doom; all right-minded persons, as we believe, must experience a feeling of satisfaction that a villain so inhuman is soon to meet his deserts. That feeling is, in our opinion, legitimate and praiseworthy. It springs from an instinct implanted in our nature, and which constitutes one of the strongest and most valuable of the great permanent bulwarks of society — the instinct that justice ought to be retributive and that abominable crimes rightly deserve the hatred of the community.
>
> Neill has been convicted of one murder only, but it is morally certain that he is guilty of all the four murders for which he was indicted, and of an attempt to murder the woman Harvey.
>
> The history of his career, or rather of the brief portion of his career which was discussed in the witness-box, is of a kind which is not easy to discuss in decent language, but it is not without its own terrible lessons. It reveals, as the career of Deeming revealed some months ago, the depths of depravity and cruelty which exist in the human heart. It demonstrates what too many amiable persons, who have no practical acquaintance with misery and with crime, are in these days inclined through a false and misguided benevolence to doubt and to deny, that there does exist amongst us a certain number of moral monsters whom it is the first duty of society to hunt down and to destroy. They are to all appearance utterly devoid of moral sense. Their one object in life is to gratify their own evil passions, and they pursue that object wholly regardless of the sufferings of their fellows, without scruple and without remorse. It has been shown in repeated instances that wretches of this kind, who are insensible to every other motive for restraining their criminal appetites, quail before the threat of corporal punishment, and in particular

before the threat of death. But even if this were not the case, it is our right and our duty to exterminate them upon proof of their guilt. They are enemies of their race, and society is bound, in duty to its weaker members, to mete out to them the measure they have meted out to others.

Mr Aitcheson, the optician who had fitted Cream with glasses, wrote the following not uninteresting letter published in *The Times* of 27 October.

47 Fleet Street,
London, E.C.
22 October

Sir,

The total disappearance of moral sense from the man Neill, now under sentence of death for the murder of Matilda Clover, has been freely attributed to his indulgence in opiates, which it is not denied he made use of in excessive quantities. But the original cause of the nervous break-up, which rendered opiates almost necessary to the man's existence, has been entirely overlooked, and as the same cause is operating in the same direction in hundreds of other cases today, you may perhaps be kind enough to allow me to draw attention to it.

Whatever the doctors may say to the contrary notwithstanding, to the defective eyesight from which Neill has suffered all his life may actually, though by the somewhat indirect process I have indicated, be attributed the very crimes for which justice is now rightly exacting the death penalty.

When Neill came to me for treatment I was able by the application of ordinary methods to determine that the defect had been of lifelong duration, and that an incalculable amount of harm might have been obviated if his eyes had been corrected in early childhood. The original defect in the left eye is hypermetropia — i.e. the optic axis of the eye is too short, and thus the rays of light do not focus perfectly on the retina; but would focus properly (if they were not stopped in progress) at a point beyond the

167

retina. A child suffering from this defect unconsciously puts a great strain on the accommodation in trying to correct it. Convergence naturally follows, and as years go on this strain is found to cause headaches and nervous pains. This would especially be the case when the eyes have to be used much for study, as in the instance of a man studying for the medical profession; and that Neill had a considerable knowledge of medical matters, gained undoubtedly by continuous study, no person who came in contact with him failed to discover.

The average doctor, I know, puts these head troubles down to any cause but the right one, and the result, as I can vouch for in hundreds of cases that have come under my notice, is that the use of drugs and sedatives becomes absolutely necessary, and, accentuating defects already existing in the eyes, produces changes in the moral nature which sometimes evidence their progress in ways that are startling and repulsive.

I remain, Yours truly,

J. AITCHESON

This ingenious letter brought down on the head of its author many indignant comments from people with defective eyesight, who apparently imagined that he had stated that such a defect must necessarily give a tendency to criminality; to which he replied that all he had meant was that the neglect of Cream's eyes in infancy was a primary cause of that 'moral anarchy' which had brought him to the condemned cell.

There is certainly no doubt that Cream suffered badly from pains in his head and drugged himself heavily in consequence, but the roots of what Mr Aitcheson called his 'moral anarchy' lay deeper than the optic nerve.

The murder of Matilda Clover had not been Cream's first incursion into crime. He had already been implicated in the deaths of two women in America, but in each case the evidence against him had not been considered strong enough, and he had escaped justice. He had actually been found guilty of the murder by strychnine of the elderly husband of a mistress of his, and had been sentenced to imprisonment for life — in spite of the fact that he had tried to throw all the blame upon the woman; unfortunately this sentence was commuted to seventeen years and then was further shortened by an allowance for 'good conduct'.

So, amazing as it may seem, this human tiger, who, besides having been found guilty of murder, was known to be a professional abortionist and a writer of scurrilous and obscene letters, was let loose upon the world once more: and at least four women in England paid with their lives for this mistaken clemency.

Cream was executed at nine o'clock in the morning of Wednesday, 16 November. He made no confession, nor referred in any way to the crimes with which he had been charged. Thus there died at the age of forty-two this extraordinary criminal, whose crimes seemed mad and yet were not without method, and whose whole plane of consciousness seems to have been so gross and debased that it is difficult to think of him as a human being and insulting to the animals to class him as one of them. He stands out in the annals of criminology as one of that fantastically evil group which contains such figures as Jegado, Zwanziger, and Van der Linden, and among these he is chiefly remarkable for the fact that killers suffering from the power mania have generally been women — unless, indeed, killing on the Nazi scale is considered to be an extreme example of the same instinct.

Doctor Satan

RAYNER HEPPENSTALL

MARCEL PETIOT, early in trouble with the juvenile courts and a great nuisance to the French Army while he served in it during the Great War, nevertheless subsequently qualified medically and took a practice in Villeneuve-sur-Yonne, fifty miles south-east of Paris, and close to the town of Auxerre, where he had been born, the son of a postman, in 1897. In 1927, a Socialist, he was elected mayor of the commune. This was odd, for although many liked him, ugly rumours circulated about the disappearance the previous year of a servant girl pregnant by him. Also in 1927, he married a woman from a neighbouring village, Georgette Lablais, who did not long delay conceiving a son.

On 14 April 1936, Dr Petiot was arrested for the theft of a book from a bookshop in the Boulevard St Michel, the Paris students' familiar Boul' Mich' on the Left Bank. He said that he had taken it absent-mindedly, its interest for him being that he thought it might help his researches into the possibility of a pump for extracting hardened faeces from the constipated. In court, psychiatric grounds were invoked, and Dr Petiot was confined at Ivry, for how long seems obscure. When we see him again, in 1940, he is in practice in the Rue de Caumartin, without a stain on his medical character and not in the least short of money.

The Rue Le Sueur lies in a residential area to the west of Paris proper, as it might be the better parts of Bayswater,

170

with Marble Arch taking the place of the Arc de Triomphe.
No 21 had once housed the famous actress Cécile Sorel. It
was up for sale in the latter half of 1940, shortly after the
Nazi occupation of Paris, when property values in the city
were low. It was bought, in the name of his son, by Dr
Petiot, who was practising in the Rue de Caumartin,
nowhere near the Rue Le Sueur. Certain structural alterations were carried out the following year. A wall was
raised at the back and a surgery built there, with double
doors and soundproofed partitions. The yard was full of
planks, cement and lime. The twelve windows on the street
remained shuttered, however, and the new owner was
rarely seen.

In the Rue de Caumartin, at No 69, three doors away from
the premises mainly used by Dr Petiot, was a furrier's,
Guschinow & Gouédo. Towards the end of 1941, Joachim
Guschinow, a Polish Jew, consulted Petiot about a
shameful disease. The really bad time for Jews in France
had not yet started, but Guschinow was anxious, and Dr
Petiot said that he knew of an organisation which, for a
consideration, would get anyone in danger first into the so-
far-still-unoccupied southern half of France, then into
Spain and thereafter to South America. On 2 January 1942,
Joachim Guschinow packed his clothes and some valuables
and, taking plenty of money, including dollar bills sewn
into the shoulder-pads of his jackets, from which any identification marks had been removed, set off for a mysterious
appointment in a street off the Rue Le Sueur. He was never
to be seen again, though messages convincing to his wife
continued to reach her through the intermediary of the
doctor.

On 19 February, a former prostitute and her well-to-do
and comparatively respectable gentleman-friend, Jean-
Pierre van Bever, were arrested on a drug charge, she being
a recognised heroin addict who, however, had been getting
prescriptions from five doctors, of whom Petiot was one.
Van Bever was conditionally released on 15 March. Next

day, another young woman addict was arrested, the daughter of a Mme Khait, not herself Jewish, though her third husband was. The girl also was a patient of Dr Petiot's. Van Bever disappeared on 22 March, Mme Khait on 25 March. Nobody inquired after the former, and Petiot contrived to allay M Khait's suspicions with supposed messages from the unoccupied zone until such time as M Khait was arrested and sent to a concentration camp where he died. On 26 May, Petiot himself was called in for questioning about the two drug cases, but released. The reader may like to know that a death in Villeneuve-sur-Yonne, while Dr Petiot was mayor of that town, had also been that of a person expected to give evidence in a case pending against him.

On 5 June disappeared a young married woman from the country south-west of Paris, Denise Hotin, on whom Petiot had performed an abortion the previous year and who had come to see him again for what reason we know not. On 20 June, a Jewish colleague, Dr Paul Braunberger, in hourly expectation of being forbidden to practice, was last seen setting off for an appointment outside the Étoile underground station, the nearest to the Rue Le Sueur. On 20 July, a family of three Knellers disappeared: Jews, of course. Then a new type of customer appeared and disappeared, ponces and their women. There were five of them, two men and three women, all friends. They disappeared in two batches in July and August 1942. It is uncertain whether the trouble they had been in was with one or other police or with colleagues and competitors in the *milieu*.

On 12 September, Mme Braunberger reported her husband's disappearance to the French police, with no immediate consequences. Next to go were the Wolffs, three of them. They were followed by the Basch, Ansbach and Stevens couples. That was in October. I take all these dates from an excellent little book by Ronald Seth,[1] rearranging

1. *Petiot, Victim of Chance*, Hutchinson, London, 1963.

them in chronological sequence. Mr Seth gives a fair amount of circumstantial detail in each case. One item in this puzzles me. The Ansbachs and the Stevenses, says Mr Seth, 'were living in Nice'. Perhaps it was simply that they wanted to get back to a home they had in Nice, for it seems unlikely that they would come from the Italian zone to German-occupied Paris in order to be got to, say, Bordeaux. The lack of simple chronological sequence in his narrative also leads Mr Seth to ignore the event which divides these earlier disappearances from a smaller group of later ones.

On 8 November, the Allies, mainly American, invaded North Africa to meet General Montgomery's rapidly advancing 8th Army. Three days later, the division between occupied and unoccupied zones was abolished, and German troops occupied the south of France as far east as Toulon, whose population they evacuated.

At any rate, the war itself bore a different complexion, and France as an entity was much changed, between the first long series of disappearances connected with Dr Petiot and those which were yet to come. The next recorded group, in March 1943, was again of ponces and their women, and it seems quite uncertain just where they wanted to go or by what route. There were two men and two women, and both men had been working for the Germans. One of them was known as Adrian the Basque. The other, Joseph (or Giuseppe) Piereschi, was a Marseilles Corsican who had been running a brothel for German soldiers in the Pas de Calais. The woman with him, Chinese Paulette, was a prostitute from Marseilles. The nature of the trouble they were in seems as obscure as just what their plans were for a happy future. However, interested in the 'escape route' of the man his *rabatteurs* or touts called 'Dr Eugène', they made their way two by two to the house in the Rue Le Sueur.

The last to go, at any rate that year, was Yvan Dreyfus. This was a sad and complicated affair, and Mr Seth is closely circumstantial about it. It appears that Dreyfus and three of his cousins were in the concentration camp at Compiègne, that French agents of the Gestapo managed to soak Mme Dreyfus, who was rich, of a great deal of money to get him out, and that he was then put on to one of the mysterious doctor's touts to spy out the escape route for the Germans installed at the Rue des Saussaies headquarters of the Sûreté Nationale. Yvan Dreyfus may have hoped to double-cross the Gestapo and in fact get away. He didn't. But, of course, when he disappeared, the Gestapo couldn't be sure that he hadn't got away. It seems that the *police judiciaire* at the Quai des Orfèvres were also hot on Petiots' trail at this time, but the Gestapo got there first. He was arrested in May and tortured, but did not reveal much, for the address in the Rue Le Sueur did not come to light, though it was discovered that he also owned a house in the south-eastern district of Reuilly, towards Vincennes. Then he was sent to prison at Fresnes, where he would remain for eight months. He must at once have got a message out to his brother Maurice, for, barely a week after his arrest, a lorry appeared in the Rue Le Sueur and drove away with forty-five suitcases, which it took to the Gare de Lyon, whence they continued by train to Auxerre, the Petiots' home town, and were later transported, again by lorry, thirty miles or so, to a house at Courson-les-Carrières, the property of a M Neuhausen.

Dr Petiot was released on 13 January 1944, his two 'leg' men, whose names were Fourrier and Pintard, having been set free two days earlier. There is an element of mystery about the release itself. The suggestion would later be made that Petiot must have undertaken to work for the Gestapo. It is possible also, as Mr Seth points out, that by following him, the Gestapo still hoped to discover the escape route. A Frenchwoman who worked for them was to state that she heard arrangements being made whereby the doctor's brother, Maurice Petiot, paid a large sum for his release, which of course does not contradict either suggestion about the reasons for it, though itself may have provided sufficient reason. At any rate, it appears that the Germans had still not discovered that Marcel Petiot had a house in the Rue Le Sueur, nor do French police inquiries seem to have established the connection.

During the weeks which followed, these latter were puzzled by a number of dismembered bodies fished out of the Seine. They bore signs of having been expertly dissected, as though by a doctor, but the fact may have no connection with Dr Petiot. A fact very certainly connected with him was the appearance, in early February, of a lorry in the Rue Le Sueur. This lorry bore a load of quicklime. It had come all the way from Auxerre and was the same, with the same driver, as, eight months before, had taken forty-five suitcases from Auxerre station to M Neuhausen's house at Courson-les-Carrières.

No 21's twelve windows on the street had remained shuttered. On 6 March, black smoke began to rise from its chimneys, and by the afternoon of Saturday, the 11th, it had become a public nuisance. The smell was dreadful, and the whole neighbourhood was complaining. Two policemen came, and the caretaker at No 23 had the Rue de Caumartin telephone number. Mme Petiot answered and fetched her husband. He asked whether the police had broken into the house and, being assured that they hadn't, said he'd be round in a quarter of an hour. It took him longer than that, and the fire brigade also was called. The corporal in charge of it was later to give evidence in court.

> *Witness, Cpl Boudringlin*: After I had broken a window-pane, I entered the house and, guided by the smell, went down to the basement. Near the boiler, I saw human remains. The boiler was drawing rather noisily. It was burning human flesh. I saw a hand, at the end of a skeleton arm. It looked like a woman's hand. I made haste upstairs. I opened the street door for the police and said to them: 'You'd better come and look, there's a job here for you.'

At this juncture, a dark-complexioned man in his forties rode up on a bicycle. It was Dr Petiot, but he announced

175

himself to the police as the owner's brother. He asked the police whether they were true Frenchmen, because, he said, the corpses were those either of Germans or of traitors. If the authorities had been notified, that was bad. It wasn't only *his* head, there were others involved. He was a leader in the Resistance, and this house was the headquarters of a secret network. Dr Petiot took a paper from his pocket and showed it to the policemen, though not so that they could read it. He'd better be off, he said. He'd got files at home he must destroy at once, three hundred or more.

They let him go. A *Paris-Soir* reporter who turned up was not at first given much to go on:

> Two men have been found burnt to death beside a central-heating boiler at a house in the Rue Le Sueur. Police inquiries have established that they were two tramps who had broken into the empty house and set fire to their garments as they tried to warm themselves.

The detective put in charge of the case at the Quai des Orfèvres was Superintendent Massu. He did not, as M Seth says, go round to the Rue Caumartin till next morning, but the fact does not call for an exclamation mark. Although, by comparison with our own, the French police often seem to be allowed too free a hand, French law has always been very strict about arresting, let alone breaking in, during the hours of darkness. It is true that a watch, if available, could have been posted outside the house or, with the caretaker's agreement, in his lodge or even on a landing, and it seems possible that the *police judiciaire*, themselves pro-Resistance and anti-German and perhaps half-ready to believe the story of documents which had to be destroyed if lives and operation secrets were to be saved, gave Petiot as much chance as they dared. We may, at any rate, be fairly certain that not calling till morning did not show mere negligence.

By then, there were no files, no Dr or Mme Petiot either. The caretaker had last seen them at some time after eleven the previous evening. The newspapers got their story on Monday, and there were photographs. Petiot was referred to as Dr Satan.

> This block and tackle stands over a pit twelve feet deep. The pit contains quicklime, in which are human bones. It is covered by an iron hatch. ... As may be seen, the small triangular cell is windowless. Note the peep-hole in the narrow door. This, it is believed, was the death chamber. ... The number of dismembered bodies is calculated to have been twenty or more. They had been dissected by a skilful hand.

By 20 March:

> Maurice Petiot, brother of the wanted man, a radio engineer in Auxerre, has been arrested and brought to Paris. Mme Petiot, wife of the doctor, is also in custody. She was traced to Courson-les-Carrières. At the house in which she was staying were found between forty and fifty suitcases, evidently taken there last year from Paris. They contained a wide variety of men's and women's clothes.

A few days later, the *rabatteurs*, Fourrier and Pintard, were also in custody.

Then Dr Satan slipped out of the news.

On 6 June, the Allies landed in Normandy. Among the premature Resistance operations which followed was the descent upon Tulle next day of the local *maquis* (a word which had come into use since the liberation of Corsica, *maquis* being the traditionally bandit-infested scrub of the island's interior). Moving north at that moment, to join in the defence of Normandy, was the *Reich* SS Division, which did a little hanging in Tulle before proceeding to the atrocity for which it is principally infamous, the burning of a church full of people at Oradour. An atrocity of a more personal nature was committed on the outskirts of Paris on 26 June. This was the taking 'for a ride' of an inspector of the Quai des Orfèvres vice squad, Henri Ricordeau, a man active in the Resistance, who was pushed out of the car, had five bullets put into him and the car's wheels driven over him in the Clamart woods (he recovered). The abductors were French gestapists, and their trigger-happy leader was Pierre Loutrel, who, as 'Pierrot le Fou', was to become known as the deadliest individual killer in France during the next two and a half years, abducting among others, though not with similar intention or results, the film actress Martine Carol.

On the morning of the last day of July, the airman-writer Antoine de St Exupéry, took off on his last flight from Corsica and, so far as we know, was blown out of the sky over the Mediterranean or the Alps. On 24 August, Paris was liberated from within, by none with more gallantry than the police, of whom more than two hundred were killed. Two days later, troops under General Leclerc entered the city.

Dr Satan was back in the news on 19 September, when *Résistance* published an article claiming to show that he had been a Nazi agent. It was headed PETIOT, SOLDIER OF THE REICH, and assumed that he would now be beyond the Rhine with the retreating German armies. Foolishly, the doctor reacted. His lawyer (at that moment engaged with the interests of his brother and of Mme Petiot) received a letter with a Paris postmark, enclosing a reply to the article. This appeared on 18 October.

> Dr Petiot rebuts the suggestion that he was ever a collaborator. The source of your columnist's information can never have existed, except perhaps in the imagination of the police. Throughout the Occupation, Dr Petiot was an active resistant, and, as the police know, he was imprisoned by the Gestapo. The moment he was released from Fresnes, he resumed his former place in the Resistance under a new codename. He demanded to be given the most active part to play, so that he might avenge the hundreds of thousands of Frenchmen tortured and killed by the Nazis. Despite the threat of prosecution which hangs over his head, he remains in touch with his friends and

is still playing an active part in the Liberation. A
friend showed him your newspaper. Deprived of all
but life and honour, he lives and serves under a false
name, awaiting the day when tongues and pens
unfettered shall declare the truth which might be so
easily discovered.

MARCEL PETIOT

The document was handwritten. It was passed to FFI
(that is to say, French Forces of the Interior) headquarters
in the Paris region, who found that the handwriting
resembled that of the reports of a Captain Valéry in the
Reuilly neighbourhood, where Petiot owned a house. On
the 31st, Petiot was arrested by an FFI captain who was in
fact as phoney as himself. On 2 November, however, he
was turned over to Superintendent Massu at the Quai des
Orfèvres. He had grown a black beard, was thin and
liverish, and looked indeed truly satanic, mad. He was told
that he was suspected of no fewer than sixty-two murders.
That was wrong, he said. The number of his victims was
sixty-three, every one of them either a German or a traitor.
Among the documents found on him was a Communist
Party card, though we cannot be certain of the significance
of that fact.

The Germans were making their last stand in Alsace.
That month, their rearguard left Strasbourg and crossed the
Rhine by the pinnacled Kehl bridge. To this day, a little
way upstream on the French side, stands a rough-hewn slab
of pink stone, polished on one side and bearing the names
of nine men murdered at that point, their bodies thrown
into the great river, by the departing Gestapo, who then
crossed over to Kehl, leaving engineers to blow the bridge
up. All crimes committed in France thereafter would lie
within the jurisdiction of French courts, even if for the
moment too many of these were the hurriedly improvised
and vengeful *cours de justice* and even if too many of the
murders which proclaimed themselves executions never
came into court.

The *épuration* or purge was under way, and very nasty

reading much of it made. Two of its earlier and, certainly, unregretted victims were eminent policemen. They were at least brought to a form of trial before they were shot on 27 December 1944, and that is more than could be said, abroad, for Mussolini and the unfortunate Clara Petacci, shot and strung up ten days before the lights came on in the better parts of Europe. Not that a public trial always guarantees justice, as we were to see at Nuremberg.

Petiot was charged with the murder of twenty-seven people. He admitted nineteen of these, the ponces and their women and some of the Jews, who also, he said, had been working for the Gestapo. He further claimed to have killed many Germans and collaborators not named in the indictment. The trial began on 18 March 1946, a Monday, and was to continue for almost three weeks.

To the right of the dock, past the clerk of the court, were stacked forty-seven suitcases and hold-alls, so that the courtroom looked a bit like the left-luggage office of a railway station. Among the contents of the suitcases (it is among the merits of Mr Seth's account that he gives us an inventory of these) were indeed several German uniforms. Below the dock sat Maître René Floriot and his four juniors, for the defence. Opposite sat no fewer than eleven black-gowned advocates for the civil complainants. In the public ministry horse-box sat the prosecuting magistrate, M Dupin, red-gowned. An usher called the gentlemen to their feet, and there entered the president of the court, Councillor Leser, and his two assessors, also red-gowned. Through a little door at the back of the dock appeared the accused with two policemen, one of whom unclicked the handcuffs. All those with seats sat down.

Dr Satan no longer had a beard. He wore a double-breasted jacket and a bow-tie: a dapper man, though with a touch of the artist (a pianist, say) in the length of his dark hair, which waves slightly. His complexion is sallow, his eyes rather hollow. There is a contemptuous twist to his mouth. He seems quite at his ease. He is not an attractive figure, but hardly the monster that people expected. A jury of seven is empanelled and sworn. The witnesses are sworn and withdraw. The clerk of the court reads the long indictment or *acte d'accusation*, which in effect is an opening speech for the prosecution.

The defendant is called to his feet, and the *interrogatoire* begins.

> *President of the Court, M Leser*: Your name is Marcel-André-Henri-Félix Petiot, married and the father of one child, a son. By profession you are a doctor of medicine. You were born at Auxerre, Yonne, on 17 January 1897. Your father, a post-office employee, died when you were eight, your mother five years later, whereupon you and a younger brother, Maurice, were confided to the care of an aunt. As a child, you were noted for your fits of violent temper.
>
> *Petiot*: Oh, come now, if we start like this, we shan't get on very well.
>
> *President*: At the age of sixteen, you came before the juvenile court in Auxerre on a charge of robbing letter-boxes, but were discharged.
>
> *Petiot*: That's better.
>
> *President*: Your scholastic record was excellent, and on leaving school at eighteen you began to study medicine, but in January 1916 were called up into the Army. You served in the 89th Infantry. Wounded in the foot by a hand-grenade in 1917. ... Is that right?
>
> *Petiot*: It wasn't serious. I can walk.
>
> *President*: You were nevertheless awarded a disability pension. You were finally discharged in 1920 on psychiatric grounds, first pleaded in your defence at a court martial in 1918, when you were accused of stealing drugs from a casualty clearing-station and selling these to your own private profit. Shall I stop there?
>
> *Petiot*: No, go on.
>
> *President*: Having completed your medical studies, you set up in private practice in 1924 in Villeneuve-sur-Yonne. Three years later, you were elected mayor of that town as a candidate of the Left. That year, you

married Georgette Lablais, and your son, Gérard, was born the following year. At various times, you were charged with the diversion of electric power to the detriment of the municipality and with theft of petrol from the railway sidings.

Petiot: The charges were dropped.

President: You were also questioned in connection with two mysterious disappearances. A charge was brought in connection with one of these, that of Mme Debauve.

Petiot: She'd been claiming to have had sexual intercourse with me. I declined the honour.

President: The gentleman who brought the charge died suddenly. He was a patient of yours.

Petiot: It happens on occasion.

President: The local gossip became such that you judged it desirable to leave Villeneuve. That was thirteen years ago. You settled in Paris, at No 66 Rue de Caumartin. You put up your plate, and you issued a prospectus, which I propose to read to the court. *(He does so.)*

Petiot: Thanks for the publicity.

President: It was the prospectus of a quack. You boasted of earning astronomical sums, but your tax-returns did not show these.

Petiot: That is traditional. When a surgeon makes millions, he declares a quarter. It proves how French I am.

President: Three years later, on being charged with the theft of a book in the Boulevard St Michel, you pleaded madness, as on previous occasions.

Petiot: You never know how mad you are. It's all a matter of comparison.

President: At any rate, by 1941, a year after the German occupation of Paris, you had made enough to buy a house in the Rue Le Sueur.

Petiot: Houses were cheap then.

President: And you caused certain alterations to be made.

Petiot: I see that we are coming to the famous 'ante-room of death'. It was intended for radiotherapy. The apparatus was at that time unobtainable.

President: It contained a bell which did not ring.

Petiot: Electric wire also was unobtainable.

President: It further contained a false door which did not lead anywhere.

Petiot: It made the room look more comfortable.

President: And in the real door was a spy-hole.

Petiot: It was papered over.

President: There was also a lime-pit. Those whose bodies were found in this pit had met their deaths by one means or another.

Petiot: The bodies were there when I came out of Fresnes. My comrades in the Resistance had to have somewhere to dispose of the traitors they had executed.

President: Who were these comrades?

Petiot: I shall not give their names. There were members of my group who wanted to come here and testify. I would not let them. On men who deserve the Liberation cross you would put handcuffs. And there's no need for you to throw your arms up in the air.

President: I shall raise my arms if I want to.

Petiot: Well, you'll be raising them higher presently. I was in the Resistance from the time the Germans arrived.

President: In your earlier statements, you gave the name of your supposed organisation as 'Fly-tox'. That is the name of a common insecticide, isn't it?

Petiot: That's what the organisation was, a common insecticide.

President: No mention of such an organisation has been found in FFI records or elsewhere. Tomorrow, I shall ask just what you did ....

Petiot: You'd do better to ask me what I didn't do. I blew up trains full of Germans. I ....

President: ... But now we shall adjourn.

Petiot: Why? I'm not tired.

Tuesday, 19 March:

Petiot: ... When we discovered an informer, we'd arrest him, pretending to be German police. The fellow would say: 'That's all right. I'm one of you.' That put an end to all doubt. We questioned him and then took him in a truck to the forest of Marly.

President: Not to the Rue Le Sueur?

Petiot: We only went there if there was some need to hurry.

For the Prosecution, M Dupin: And, in the forest of Marly, what exactly did you do to your prisoner?

Petiot: Got sadistic tastes, have you? These traitors were executed and buried, that's all you need to know. When I'm acquitted ....

Dupin: Acquitted? You?

Petiot: I'm counting on it. It won't be you who judge me, it'll be the gentlemen of the jury. In them I have confidence. I got my hands dirty all right, but I didn't soil them by holding them up to swear oaths of allegiance to Pétain.

President: Everybody knows under what conditions. Don't be insolent.

Petiot: To whom? To Pétain?

In 1940, a formal declaration of allegiance to the new constitution under the government formed at Vichy had indeed been required of all State employees. With whatever mental reservations, most State employees had made it and thus remained at their posts. In distant retrospect, it must be clear to all but juveniles and a lunatic fringe on the Left that they had been right to do so, but in 1946 it was less clear to many who yet were neither utter fools nor interested parties. It would be nice to have a stereophonic recording of court reaction at this juncture in the Petiot trial. It is specifically enjoined upon French jurymen that they must not allow what they feel to appear even from their facial expressions.

On Wednesday, 20 March, the disappearances, in the summer of 1942, of Dr Braunberger and the Knellers were considered. Petiot claimed to have heard from both after their escapes, from Braunberger in South America, from the Knellers in Bordeaux and thereafter. The Knellers had had a son, René, with them.

Petiot: Yes, he was a nice little boy.

President: In one of those suitcases, the boy's pyjamas were found.

Petiot: They were dirty, and they had his initials on them. His mother said he should leave them.

Next day, it was the turn of the ponces and their women. Petiot admitted killing Adrian the Basque and three Corsicans, with four of their women, including Chinese Paulette, but not that any of these had been among the bodies found in the Rue Le Sueur.

Petiot: ... We didn't need to question Adrian. We knew his rotten mug. We stuck a revolver into his back to make him climb into the truck. He pulled a knife. It was like a butcher's shop.

Dupin: Was it necessary to execute the women?

Petiot: They'd have given us away. What do you think we ought to have done with them?

President: The Wolffs, the Ansbachs, the Stevenses, they were not criminals. They were Jews who were hiding from the Nazis.

Petiot: They were Germans. They'd been told to hide. When I was first married, I used to hide under the sheets and say to my wife: 'Come and find me!' That's the way they were hiding.

President: And Yvan Dreyfus?

Petiot: A traitor to his race, his religion and his country.

But Petiot denied that any of these were among the bodies found at the Rue Le Sueur. The following morning, Friday the 22nd, those premises were visited by the whole court, the lawyers, the jury, twelve car-loads altogether. The road had been blocked, but people leaned out of upstairs windows, and a crowd had gathered outside the barriers. There being no electricity in the house, those who descended to the basement had to make do with a police inspector's taper: quite enough, as Petiot said, to enlighten the law. The walls of the triangular room were exceptionally thick. They'd deaden any cries, said Dupin. They had to be thick, said Petiot, for protection against x-rays. Lead had been quite impossible to obtain. As the court might easily see, there was no space to kill anyone in that room. Nor, suggested Dupin, was there room to practise radiotherapy. Once the apparatus had been installed, where would the patient lie? Councillor Leser thought it curious that, with so many rooms in the house, the doctor should have set up his consulting room in an outbuilding at the rear of the basement.

The crowd had already brought in its verdict, and the twelve cars drove away to a chorus of hostile shouts. In court, during the afternoon, the chief expert witness was called, the French Sir Bernard Spilsbury, Dr Paul, white-moustached, fat, old, as often made a fool of by clever defending counsel as his English counterpart, the one real-life character to whom, in his novels, M Simenon gives no fictitious name.

> *President*: Dr Paul, you examined all the remains that were found two years ago in the Rue Le Sueur. In your view, how did those people die?
> *Dr Paul*: It cannot be established. It was not by a bullet or a blow on the head, that is certain. Asphyxiation, strangling, poison, a knife-wound — all those are possible.
> *President*: Injections?
> *Dr Paul*: It is possible, but I must not theorise.
> *President*: Might gas have been used?
> *Dr Paul*: Again, it is possible. Not coal gas, however. The discolouration produced by carbon-monoxide poisoning would have been apparent in the fragments of skin which remained.
> *President*: The bodies had been skilfully dissected?
> *Dr Paul*: The man had a knowledge of anatomy. I said to M Goletty, 'A doctor has done this. Pray God it was not one of my pupils.'
> *For the Defence, Maître Floriot*: Mr President ... I don't know whether Dr Paul is aware of the fact that, during his medical training, my client never followed any course in dissection.

Dr Paul: That surprises me. It's a pity, too. He dissects very well.

Floriot: Excuse me, Dr Paul, what we must say is that the dissector, whoever he may have been, dissects very well.

At Saturday's hearing and all the second week and again on the following Monday, 1 April, some eighty witnesses were heard. They included relatives and friends of those who had disappeared, as well as the touts who had sent people to 'Dr Eugène'. There were also psychiatrists and handwriting-experts. Among witnesses for the defence was a Richard Lhéritier, who'd been trained in England and parachuted into France by the RAF. He'd been captured and had spent five months in Fresnes with Petiot.

President: You were sharing a cell?

Lhéritier: Yes.

President: And what impression did you form of your enforced companion?

Lhéritier: I found Dr Petiot an intelligent man. He gave me very good advice on how to behave under torture. He raised everybody's morale. He passed messages out of prison, and he gave me safe addresses I could go to if I escaped.

President: Did he speak to you about his alleged work in the Resistance?

Lhéritier: Constantly.

President: What did you think about it?

Lhéritier: He wasn't working alone, he worked for a party, which gave him orders.

President: A party of the Left?

Lhéritier: Yes.

President: Did you learn the code-name of his organisation?

Lhéritier: Yes.

President: What was it?

Lhéritier: 'Fly-tox'.

Maître Floriot: It has been suggested that no such group existed, that Petiot invented it after the discoveries in the Rue Le Sueur.

Lhéritier: No.

Floriot: He talked to you about a group under that name?

Lhéritier: Yes, about that and about his escape route.

Floriot: You spent five months together. Do you think that a man can hide his true feelings as long as that?

Lhéritier: You can't share a cell for long and not know your companion.

Petiot: Lhéritier, do you think that any sane man could accuse me of working for the Gestapo?

Lhéritier: No. ... Mr President, whatever the result of this trial may be, I shall always recall with gratitude that I shared a cell with Dr Petiot.

And there were others who testified that he'd made out false medical certificates to keep them from being deported and that he'd got warnings out to Jewish families when they were in danger.

During the first week of the trial, the courtroom had been crowded. The crowd dropped off during the second week. There were very few there when on Tuesday of the third week, 2 April, the lawyers in the civil action began (a thing which, of course, doesn't happen in British criminal proceedings). They were very tedious, especially the barrister representing the family of Chinese Paulette, who no doubt hoped for handsome damages and who were not in the least Chinese. Petiot sketched these lawyers and wrote a poem about them, understandably savage and not unamusing. He'd been doing a good deal of writing in prison — in prose, a treatise on the laws of chance and how to overcome them (it was later published). One of these lawyers, the most effective of them, Maître Véron, ventured a notable image.

Véron: You knew the legend of the wreckers, those cruel men who lit fires on the cliffs designed to lure mariners in distress into the belief that they'd found a haven of refuge. Unable to imagine that any such blackness of heart existed, the steersman landed his vessel on the rocks, with the loss of all souls aboard and all that they owned. Those very men who gave the illusion of safety enriched themselves with the spoils. Well! that's what Petiot was: the false saviour, the false refuge. He attracted people to him as though to save them. He murdered and despoiled them!

On the afternoon of the 3rd, the crowd began to drift back. Shortly before half-past five, red-robed M Dupin began his concluding speech for the prosecution. He continued next morning. With brilliant timing, the defendant spoiled his peroration.

> *Dupin*: ... But we shall no longer let Petiot foul the sacred name of the Resistance ....
> *Petiot*: Signed: State Prosecutor of France.
> *Dupin*: Petiot, the role of administrator of justice hardly becomes you.
> *Petiot*: What about yourself?
> *Dupin*: ... Gentlemen, let Petiot go from here to join his victims!

Maître Floriot followed for the defence. He spoke for almost seven hours, and by all accounts it was magnificent. At half-past nine, court and jury retired. The court — that is to say, the presiding judge and the two assessors by whom, throughout the proceedings, he had sat dumbly flanked — retired with the jury. This practice had been established under the government of Vichy, which had also reduced the numbers of jurors from twelve to seven. Together with the three red-robed *magistrats*, who were not supposed to attempt to lead the argument but merely to answer questions of law, they deliberated for well over two hours, with three questions to answer in respect of each of the twenty-seven murders alleged. Floriot also retired, to replenish his forces in the barristers' refreshment-room. Returning to the cells below the dock, he expected to find his client agitated and in need of calming words. Petiot was sleeping peacefully. When the court again took its place and the jury came in with the verdict a little before midnight, he had to be awakened to be taken up to the dock again.

He was found guilty, without mitigating circumstances, of wilful murder upon all but one of the twenty-seven persons with whose deaths he was charged. He listened to the verdict and to the sentence of death contemptuously, but, as he was led away once more, called out: 'You must avenge me!' It is not known to whom he called, whether to his wife and son (she, certainly, had been sitting in court and now rose) or to the public at large or to a group of friends among the public. It is also unknown on whom revenge was to be wreaked.

On Wednesday, 15 May, Petiot's appeal was rejected by the Court of Cassation. By Friday, 24 May, the Fourth Republic had not yet elected a President, and so the appeal to presidential clemency was void. At a quarter to five on the morning of Saturday, 25 May, Marcel-André-Henri-Félix Petiot, then in his fiftieth year, was awakened and enjoined, in the customary formula, to have courage, which he had.

In his book on miscarriage of justice,[1] Maître Floriot does not instance the trial of Dr Petiot, and so I suppose that he thinks his most famous client was guilty as charged and found. He is on record as saying that, among all the murderers he has known, Petiot alone was a man of intelligence.

Not long after trial and execution, the house in the Rue Le Sueur was pulled down. There was still no trace of any of the valuables and money which had presumably passed through the doctor's hands, estimated to be worth something like a quarter of a million pounds sterling. If I have understood him properly, Mr Seth's theory is that they went to swell Communist Party funds. During the first year of the Occupation, the French communists collaborated, as far as the occupying forces would allow them to do so. Only when the Germans invaded Russia did communists first play any part in the Resistance, which all

1. *When Justice Falters* (translated by Rayner Heppenstall), Harrap, London 1972.

too soon they came to dominate. According to Mr Seth, it was members of the communist Resistance, possibly including another doctor, who dumped bodies at the Rue Le Sueur while Petiot was in prison. On his release in early 1944, finding them in his lime-pit, he said, 'Ah, well!' and, being told to get on with it, started to burn them. The reason why he didn't talk, at or before his trial, was that threats had been made against his wife and son if he did. *He* was 'for it' anyway and had only one head to lose.

The Polite Doctor Pritchard

H. M. WALBROOK

EDWARD WILLIAM PRITCHARD, a physician who described himself in the *Medical Directory* for 1865 as a member of the Royal College of Surgeons and as holding a foreign degree of MD, was an Englishman who had been born at Southsea in 1815. His father and other male relations had been in the Royal Navy, and in his early twenties he held a medical appointment in that service and saw much of the world, from the countries bordering on the Mediterranean to those washed by the Polar and Pacific Seas.

In the year 1850 he married a Miss Mary Jane Taylor, the daughter of a Glasgow silk merchant of position, and found himself fortunate in the possession not only of a fond wife, but also of a devoted mother-in-law, Mrs Taylor, a lady who possessed means of her own and who made quite an idol of her daughter's pleasant-mannered husband. His wife's relations exerted themselves successfully to release him from the Navy and find a practice for him at home, and for a time he worked professionally at Hunmanby and Filey in Yorkshire. In 1859 he moved to Glasgow and spent the remainder of his professional career there.

In the early months of 1865 we find him occupying a house in Clarence Place, Sauchiehall Street, towards the purchase of which his mother-in-law had advanced him £500, a fifth of which, incidentally, he put into his own pocket instead of handing it over to the vendors. By this time he had a family of five young children, to whom he was an apparently devoted parent.

Nearly six feet in height, he may well have cut a majestic figure in the Glasgow drawing-rooms of his day. He wore an enormous light brown beard; the upper part of his capacious head was impressively bald, and his athletic frame was distinguished by what is called a scholar's stoop. Some people, however, seemed to find his manner too propitiatory to be pleasant. Like the King in *Hamlet*, he was apparently one of those who could 'smile and smile'. For some reason or other, his professional brethren seemed rather to dislike him. Nor was his reputation among his female patients one of the best; and when at last his crash came, an ungoverned lust for a young servant-girl in his own employ played a conspicuous part in it.

Like many other eminent criminals, he was inordinately vain. He was very proud of the fine beard, which he combed and trimmed with pomatum every morning. He was also fond of being photographed, and had a weakness for distributing his portrait to people on short acquaintance. And he particularly enjoyed the self-advertisement of the lecturing platform. Two of his favourite subjects of discourse were 'Egypt and its Climate' and 'Pitcairn Island'. Furthermore, he was the author of a number of magazine articles on such topics as 'The Use and Abuse of Tobacco', 'Normal Sleep' and 'Longevity'.

The scene of the crimes which brought him to the scaffold was the house already mentioned in Sauchiehall Street. Before moving into it he had passed through an unpleasant experience in an earlier residence in the same city, where a bedroom had caught fire, a servant-girl had been burned to death, and the doctor's prompt claim on the insurance company for damages had been politely but firmly turned down. This incident had provoked a good deal of comment of a more or less public sort. At the time of his move to Sauchiehall Street, moreover, his two banking accounts were overdrawn. As he arranged to let a couple of the bedrooms to lodgers, it seems likely that Mrs Pritchard was not unaware of his monetary difficulties. There he was, however, in a very nice house, with his comely wife, four of his young children — the fifth was staying with her grandmamma, old Mrs Taylor, in Edinburgh — and a couple of servants, Lattimer the cook, and Mary McLeod, a good-looking girl of between sixteen and seventeen, who acted as housemaid and nurse.

Soon after the moving-in, another unpleasant incident occurred. Mrs Pritchard caught her husband in the act of kissing the young housemaid in one of the bedrooms. The damsel exhibited much distress at the discovery and entreated her mistress to give her notice and let her go. Mrs Pritchard, however, evidently liked her. She took a lenient view of the matter, said she would give the doctor a 'talking to' on his behaviour, and permitted the girl to continue in her service. It is not known what form her remonstrance with the doctor took, but it is very definitely established that it had not the smallest effect upon his conduct. It afterwards came out that he had already seduced the girl, that he had given her a drug to procure abortion, and that his immoral relationship with her was continued as long as he was a free man.

Thus we find him in the February of 1865, a doctor rather under a cloud, short of money, and carrying on a surreptitious love-affair with one of his own servants, whom he had privately assured that if his wife should happen to die, he would make her the second Mrs Pritchard.

At the time we speak of he had evidently decided that the sooner the former of these events happened the better. With his professional knowledge, he fixed on antimony in the form of tartar emetic as a safe and certain way out of his conjugal bonds, and purchased large quantities of that poison from local druggists. He also decided not to kill Mrs Pritchard with a single dose, though it would have been quite easy to do so, for she was by no means robust. Such a procedure might, however, arouse suspicion. His plan, therefore, was to administer small doses at intervals of a couple of days or so, of which the effect would be that one day she would be apparently very ill, the next she would seem better, the day after worse again, and so on, growing steadily weaker all the time, and enduring from week to week the maximum of pain and anguish. As usual, there were flaws in the procedure. He behaved like an idiot, for instance, in not buying his poisons in some other city and under some other name. But on the whole it was a fairly cleverly thought-out scheme, and for a time it worked as well as he could have wished.

On the evening of 1 February, the cook, Lattimer, was rung for by her mistress, and on going up to her room found the lady very ill, suffering from cramp in her hands and down her side, complaining of vomiting, and in dreadful pain. Next day she was better. A night or two later, a scream rang through the house at midnight and, on hurrying up, the servant found her in a condition of high excitement, with her husband standing beside the bed endeavouring to soothe her. Again she got better, and presently she seemed well enough to leave home on a few days' visit to her mother in Edinburgh. Under Mr and Mrs Taylor's roof she made a visible recovery from her mysterious illness, and wrote home cheerfully and hopefully.

On her return to the home in Sauchiehall Street, however, all the symptoms which had previously so alarmed the household – cramp, vomiting, and acute pain – promptly reappeared. Presently, old Mrs Taylor, visibly anxious, came on a visit to the Glasgow household. She was most affectionately welcomed by her anxious son-in-law. The old lady slept in the same room with her daughter, and was equally puzzled and distressed by all that she saw. 'I don't understand Mrs Pritchard's case,' she remarked one day to the cook. 'She seems one day better and two worse!' The girl, McLeod, had also been making her observations. She noticed that her mistress now nearly always vomited after eating or drinking. Everyone in the house, too, had observed that the doctor seemed to have given up hope. Frequently he wept.

On 24 February, Mrs Taylor herself was suddenly taken alarmingly ill. The bell rang and Mary McLeod went up, to find the old lady seated in a chair, insensible, with her eyes closed and her head hanging down upon her breast. On the bed beside her lay Mrs Pritchard, now dreadfully emaciated, glaring wildly at her mother. By Dr Pritchard's orders another physician was called in. This was Dr James Paterson, a gentleman who had been in extensive practice in the city for thirty years. On his arrival, Pritchard took him first into the consulting room and told him that his mother-in-law, while in the act of writing a letter, had been suddenly taken ill and had fallen from her chair, after which she had been conveyed to the bedroom. He also mentioned that his wife was in the same room, and that she had been very poorly for a long time past as a result of gastric fever.

On entering the bedroom, Dr Paterson found the old lady and her daughter in the one bed, the former looking as if she had had a sudden seizure, and the daughter sitting up, with her hair much dishevelled. After an examination, he informed Dr Pritchard that Mrs Taylor was under the influence of some powerful narcotic, that she was dying, and that nothing could save her. He then, without comment, took a long look at the daughter, observed her exhausted look, the hectic flush on her cheeks, her semi-imbecile expression, and the weak, peculiar tone of her voice. He said nothing to Dr Pritchard; but he walked back to his house that night convinced not only that Mrs Taylor was doomed, but also that Mrs Pritchard was 'under the depressing influence of antimony'.

An hour later Mrs Taylor died, and her husband, the rich merchant, was telegraphed for and hastened to Glasgow. Next morning Pritchard, apparently prostrated with grief, persuaded his father-in-law to go round to Dr Paterson, who lived almost within a stone's throw, and request the death-certificate. Dr Paterson emphatically turned down the request. He also reminded his visitor that in any case such a certificate would have to be handed, not to a friend or relative of the deceased person, but to the Registrar. Later Dr Paterson was the recipient of a schedule from the

Registrar which he promptly returned, enclosed in the following very significant letter:

Dear Sir,

I am surprised that I am called upon to certify the *cause of death* in this case. I only saw the person a few minutes a very short period before her death. She seemed to be under some narcotic; but Dr Pritchard, who was present from the first moment until death occurred, which happened in his own house, may certify the cause. The death was certainly sudden, unexpected, and to me mysterious.

I am, dear Sir, etc.

J. PATERSON

This letter the Registrar afterwards admitted having received, but added that he was sorry to say it had not been kept! It had apparently been torn up and dropped into the waste-paper basket! Dr Pritchard, however, had no hesitation in filling up the certificate himself, declaring the cause of death to be paralysis and apoplexy. After that, Mrs Taylor's body was duly conveyed to Edinburgh, where on 2 March she was buried, her son-in-law being one of the mourners. After the funeral, a meeting of the deceased lady's relations and trustees took place, at which Dr Pritchard heard that by her will he would inherit two-thirds of her estate if his wife should happen to die before him, the money to be for the benefit of his children until they came of age, and afterwards 'for his own use as he may consider proper'. The news seems to have touched him deeply.

He then returned to his home in Sauchiehall Street and to the wife who was now mourning a mother whose funeral she had been too ill to attend. On 17 March he called once more on Dr Paterson and asked him to come round and see her. He did so, and once more he was much struck with her terrible appearance. There was a peculiarly wild expression in her face, her eyes were sunken and fiery red, and her cheeks hollow, pinched-looking and flushed. She greeted him with a half-smile of recognition, muttered something about vomiting, complained of great thirst, and 'made movements with her hands as if to clutch at some imaginary object on the bed-clothes'. When the visitor expressed his apprehensions at these symptoms, the husband mournfully mentioned that so lately as the previous day she had been in the drawing-room playing with the children. Dr Paterson's reply to this is not recorded. He left a prescription to procure sleep, and Pritchard undertook to have it made up.

At midnight — the hour at which old Mrs Taylor had died a few weeks before — Mrs Pritchard suddenly cried to her husband, 'Edward! Don't speak! Look! Do you see my mother?' An hour later there came a ring at Dr Paterson's bell. On the hall-door being opened, a messenger from Pritchard presented himself. The message brought was that there would be no further need for Dr Paterson to come to Sauchiehall Street, as Mrs Pritchard was dead. On the occasion of this second bereavement, Dr Pritchard promptly filled up the death-certificate and took it to the Registrar. It declared that the lady had died from an attack of gastric fever which had lasted two months.

This second tragedy, following so quickly upon the first, inevitably kindled suspicions. Somebody sent an anonymous letter to the authorities, a post-mortem was ordered, and it was discovered that the body of the dead woman contained 'unequivocal evidences of antimony'. It was then ordered that the body of Mrs Taylor should be exhumed and a similar investigation made. Here again the body was found saturated with the same poison and also containing evidence that a dose of aconite had been administered shortly before death.

On 22 March Dr Pritchard found himself a prisoner, charged with the murder of his wife, and on the following 21 April he was further charged with having murdered his mother-in-law. The young housemaid Mary McLeod was also apprehended as involved in her mistress's death, but after an examination before the Sheriff was allowed to go free. The doctor solemnly denied the truth of each charge,

eclared that he had never administered antimony intern-
lly to his wife or any poison whatever to Mrs Taylor, and
eiterated his conviction that the one had died of paralysis
nd apoplexy, the other of gastric fever.

The trial opened at the High Court of Justiciary,
dinburgh, on Monday 3 July 1865, before the Lord
ustice-Clerk Inglis, the great lawyer who, eight years
efore, had so brilliantly defended Madeleine Smith, and
ith him were two other ornaments of the Scottish Bench,
ords Ardmillan and Jerviswoode. The Solicitor-General
or Scotland, George Young (afterwards Lord Young), led
or the Crown, and Mr Andrew Rutherfurd Clark (after-
ards Lord Rutherfurd Clark), one of the ablest advocates
f the time, for the defence. For five days it went on before
crowded court, and as witness followed witness, the fact
hich became ever more and more obscure was the pris-
ner's motive, while the thing that glared ever more and
ore clear was his guilt. Early in the proceedings the court
eard of the footing on which he had been living with his
ervant-girl and of his promise to her. Even that, however,
id not explain his having killed his wife with such
rolonged and deliberate cruelty. The earlier murder
eemed even less explicable, for Mrs Taylor had already
roved herself a generous friend to him, and there was no
vidence that he had known beforehand of the benevolent
emembrance of him in her will.

A notable witness was Mary McLeod, and some of the
ost painful moments in the trial were those in which Mr
utherfurd Clark dragged from her the miserable story of
er seduction, of her subsequent repeated submissions to
im, and of his undertaking to marry her in the event of
is wife's death. Obviously acting on the advice of his
lient, Mr Clark plainly hinted that she had been a
articipant if not even the principal in the murders.
ounsel for the prosecution, however, had little difficulty
a demolishing the idea that a girl so young, and knowing
othing of drugs and their potencies, could, in a doctor's
ouse, week after week and month after month, make her

199

way to her master's depositories, and dose her mistress's
food with a little antimony here, a little aconite there, to
the fatal end. In his charge to the jury the Lord Justice-
Clerk also commented on the matter as follows:

> Is it conceivable that a girl of sixteen, in the position
> of a servant maid, could of herself have conceived and
> executed such a design within this house, under the
> eye and subject to the vigilance of the husband of one
> of the victims, himself a medical man? On the other
> hand, it is not so difficult to believe that she may have
> been the perfectly unconscious instrument of carrying
> out his purpose, seeing nothing but kindness on the
> part of the prisoner towards his victims. A girl in her
> position might thus be the unconscious means of
> carrying out these designs in perfect innocence.

The other notable witness was Dr James Paterson, who
was fated to cut a figure in the witness-box which rendered
him for a time at any rate almost as unpopular as the prisoner. In the first place he exhibited a definite animus not
only in his word, but also in his look and tone against the
man in the dock. His repeated allusions to him as
'Pritchard' when by Bar and Bench he was still being
courteously mentioned as 'Dr Pritchard' created an
unpleasant impression, which was deepened by his very
definite suggestion that more than once the prisoner had
deliberately lied to him. The climax of his display came
when Mr Rutherfurd Clark asked him why he had kept his
suspicions regarding Mrs Pritchard to himself. The report
of the case in the 'Notable British Trials' series gives the
passage in full, and the following is quoted from it:

> You formed the conviction that she was under the
> influence of antimony? – Yes.
> Do you mean to convey that she had been taking
> antimony medicinally or that she was being poisoned
> by antimony? – My opinion was that she was being
> poisoned by antimony.
> As you thought Mrs Pritchard was suffering in that
> way, did you ever go back to see her again? – I did not.

Why? – Because she was not my patient. I had nothing to do with her.

Is it not your duty to look after a fellow-creature whom you believe is being poisoned? – There was another doctor in the house. I did the best I could by apprising the Registrar.

You stood upon your dignity and did not go back to see what you believed to be a case of poisoning? – I had no right.

No right? – I had no power to do it.

No power? – I was under no obligation.

Having been in a house where you thought poisoning was going on, you did not consider it was your duty to go back? – I had discharged my duty so far as I thought it incumbent on me.

By prescribing certain things and not knowing whether the prescription was followed? – In any case where a consultation is held, the consulting physician has no right to go back and see the patient.

Then it was the dignity of your profession that prevented you from going back? – It is the etiquette of our profession. In any case, when I had been called in for consultation, were I to go back, it would be a breach of the etiquette of my profession.

The Lord Justice-Clerk subsequently, in addressing the jury, alluded to this exchange of questions and answers in scathing terms:

> Dr Paterson, having formed the opinion that somebody was practising upon Mrs Pritchard with poison, thought it consistent with his professional duty to keep that opinion to himself. In that I cannot say that I concur. I care not for professional etiquette or professional rule. There is a rule of life, and a consideration that is far higher than these – and that is the duty that every right-minded man owes to his neighbour to prevent the destruction of human life in this world. In that duty I cannot but say Dr Paterson failed.

These and the other strictures directed against him left Dr Paterson quite unmoved. In a long letter to the *Glasgow*

Herald a few days later, he poured forth his very unfavourable opinion of the barrister who had cross-examined him, the judge who had denounced him, and doctors other than himself who had seen Mrs Pritchard in her illness and had failed to detect what was taking place. The letter revealed the 'imperturbable Scot' to the last perfection. It did not, however, dispel the feeling that had he communicated his suspicions confidentially in the right quarter a little earlier and considered professional etiquette a little less, he might have saved an innocent life, if not two.

In the end, the jury brought in their inevitable verdict and the prisoner was sentenced to death. At this moment of crisis, all Pritchard's famous good manners came out. On being bidden to stand while judgment was being delivered, he rose and faced the Judge with much dignity. At the words 'You are aware that upon such a verdict only one sentence can be pronounced,' he politely bowed. After the words 'You must be condemned to suffer the last penalty of the law,' he bowed again, and after the concluding prayer that God Almighty might have mercy upon his soul, he bowed twice, first to the Judge and then to the jury. His remaining days were spent largely in religious exercises, and on 28 July, in the presence of a multitude said to number a hundred thousand people, he was hanged in Glasgow; it was the last public hanging in that city.

No more singular type figures in the annals of crime. Not only his manner but also his appearance were far more those of a philanthropist than of a murderer. From the various confessions he left behind him, he seems to have been as bewildered by his own wickedness as his friends had been. His mentality was the strangest muddle of cold cruelty and religious hysteria. An entry in his diary records the death of the wife whom he had so cruelly murdered:

> *Saturday 18 March 1865.* Died here at 1 am Mary Jane my own beloved wife aged 38 years — no torment surrounded her bedside — but like a calm peaceful lamb of God passed Minnie away. May God and Jesus, Holy Ghost, one in three — welcome Minnie. Prayer

on prayer till mine be o'er; everlasting love. Save us
Lord, for Thy dear Son.

What manner of man can he have been who, burdened
with the knowledge of his acts, could throw off the load
and pen this disgusting outburst of hysterical piety? One
seems to hear his sobs and howls as he wrote. One can
imagine Mary McLeod standing outside the closed door of
the consulting room listening, with what mixed feelings, to
the grief of her master and lover, the man who had promised
to marry her! It is the story of Jekyll and Hyde in real life,
with the sole difference that in this case the Jekyll was as
nauseous as the Hyde. Plausible, sensual, egotistical,
ruthless, and in every way a liar, he was a creature to be
feared. Like one of the Satanists of whom we read in the
Middle Ages, he mingled the bestial with the spiritual and
sought to marry the infernal and the divine. Such a person
could in no age be other than a public danger, and his
suppression was obviously an act of public service.

Postscript

Excerpts from a report, 'Execution of Dr Pritchard,' in the
Edinburgh Evening Courant of Saturday, 29 July 1865:

> The South Jail in Glasgow, at which the execution
> took place yesterday, is situated on the north bank of
> the Clyde and close to Hutcheson Bridge. In front of
> the building is the Green, and at the north end is Jail
> Square, into which the Saltmarket, the Bridgegate, and
> a number of lanes inhabited by the very lowest classes
> of the population converge. The portion of the Green
> immediately opposite the Jail was, during the Fair and
> up till Thursday, covered with stands, shows, shoot-
> ing booths, &c.; but by order of the magistrates they
> were all cleared away on Thursday night, with the
> exception of the circus and the old clothes market,
> which are more or less permanent. The effect of this
> clearance was that a much larger space was obtained
> by the spectators, who were much less crowded than

they would otherwise have been. No fewer than four rows of strong barriers were erected in front of the Jail, which were placed so as to break the pressure. The innermost barricade was at a considerable distance from the scaffold, and all round the Jail a large extent of ground was left clear. The public were entirely excluded from Hutcheson Bridge, which leads directly to the front of the prison, and from which a good view of the spectacle might have been obtained. It appears, however, that the bridge is in an unsafe condition, and it was considered prudent not to permit any one to go upon it.

The erection of the barricades on Thursday attracted much attention, and large numbers of people lounged in the neighbourhood of the prison all day. From about eight o'clock in the evening till midnight the crowd increased very much; and up till eleven the assemblage embraced a considerable sprinkling of respectable-looking people, but after that hour the crowd thinned considerably, and the dregs remained. Hundreds of the very lowest classes — drunkards, thieves, and vagabonds — took up their quarters for the night around the barricades. Altogether there was presented a collection of the most disreputable characters that could be seen anywhere, the greater number of whom spent the time in disturbing the neighbourhood with their yelling. The spectators during the night and early part of the morning consisted of about equal numbers of men and women. There were also, however, a good many boys and girls, and even children with their parents. Some of the more peaceably disposed lay down on the Green and slept till morning. Groups were formed, in which there were speculations as to how the prisoner would behave on the scaffold, and others joined in ribald jokes and unseemly jests. During the night there was a considerable body of police in attendance, which was largely augmented in the morning as the spectators increased in number. About one o'clock the sky became overcast, and a slight shower fell, which gave rise to apprehensions that the morning might be wet, but fortunately the rain wore off.

About two o'clock the scaffold was brought from a shed in Clyde Street, a short distance from the jail, and its appearance caused great sensation. The erection of the scaffold, which has been in use during the last fifty years, was watched with much interest. On the rope being fastened to the beam, a thrill of horror ran through the crowd. The fitting up of the scaffold was concluded about half-past three. The scaffold is a large, black-painted box, the interior of which is about twelve feet square, the sides rising three feet above the platform. The height of the beam is about eight or nine feet, and the rope was placed so as to let the culprit fall between three and four feet. The frame of the scaffold is on wheels, and is put together for the most part with bolts. The platform is reached by a broad flight of steps. Underneath the scaffold, as usual, a coffin was placed. It was a plain, black shell, and certainly appeared scarcely long enough for the body it was to contain.

A gentleman connected with the North Prison visited the prisoner on Thursday in his cell in order to bid him farewell. After some conversation the gentleman bade Dr Pritchard adieu, when the latter, shaking his friend warmly by the hand, said, 'Farewell; I am prepared to die to-morrow morning. I trust in the Lord Jesus'; and laying his hand upon one of his attendants, said to him fervently, 'Believe in the Lord Jesus Christ.' On Thursday the prisoner wrote a long letter to 'his dear Fan' — his eldest daughter. When he spoke about his children his eyes filled with tears, and he seemed overwhelmed with grief.

Dr Pritchard sat up till a late hour on Thursday night, and occupied the most of his time in reading and writing. The subject to which his mind was directed appeared to be the same as during the day, and was evidently of a religious character, as he frequently turned up passages of Scripture as he was writing. After he went to bed he slept soundly till half-past five o'clock, when he was awoke by the attendants. Although up till his last night he continued calm and composed, his pale appearance indicated that the confinement and the mental anxiety were telling upon him.

When the prisoner was awoke by his attendants he was quite tranquil, and seemed to have got refreshing sleep. He, however, partook of very little food before execution. Mr Stirling, governor of the prison, entered the cell soon after the prisoner rose, and in reply to a question put by him how he was, the wretched man, said he was 'fine'. In the words of another official he was 'brisker than on any morning since his confession'. He made reference to his approaching execution to some of those who were with him in the cell, and said that he fully allowed the justice of his sentence, and that he was prepared to go to the scaffold.

In the course of the morning, before the execution, the burying-ground for condemned criminals was visited with interest by those who had been admitted to the Jail. The burial-place is in the courtyard, which is overlooked by a large number of cells. The graves are indicated by single figures and the 'broad arrow'.

Shortly after six o'clock the Old Courtroom was opened for the proceedings that uniformly take place immediately before executions in Glasgow. It is the custom to bring the prisoner from the condemned cell to the Courtroom, and the question is put by the presiding magistrate to the culprit whether he has anything to say why the sentence of death upon him should not be carried into effect. The lower part of the Courtroom was soon filled by officials, representatives of the press, and others who had been admitted by ticket. Among those present were Councillor Bryson, Edinburgh, who came along with several other gentlemen for the purpose of taking a cast of Pritchard's head for the Phrenological Society of Edinburgh.

On the table was placed a bottle of wine in case the prisoner might be disposed to take some refreshment before being led forth for execution.

About half-past seven o'clock Executioner Calcraft appeared on the scaffold and looked about him for a minute. He was soon recognised by the assemblage, who greeted him with cheers and hisses; but there is no doubt that the cheers were more general than the hisses. After satisfying himself that the apparatus was in proper condition, he withdrew.

Precisely at eight o'clock the magistrates took their seats on the bench. The town-clerk handed to the presiding magistrate a receipt to be given to the governor of the Jail for the person of the prisoner. For a few minutes there was the utmost stillness, and an awe-inspiring feeling pervaded every one.

At five minutes past eight, after the prisoner was pinioned, prayer was offered up by Mr Oldham, the Episcopal clergyman, while the melancholy procession was moving from the condemned cell. The service, which was distinctly heard by the people above, was concluded on arriving at the foot of the stair leading to the Court. There was then a minute of breathless suspense; spectators could not be constrained to keep their places by the cry of 'Seats! Seats!'; and every person in the Court was soon standing up in order to get a look at the criminal.

It may be mentioned that before the procession left the condemned cell, an officer ran hastily downstairs with two letters, which were said to be for the prisoner.

Mr Stirling, Governor of the prison, was the first to step on the floor of the Court. He was followed by the Rev Mr Oldham, the Rev Mr Doran, the Rev Dr Macleod, and the jailer. The prisoner came immediately after the jailer, accompanied by two or three policemen, and followed by Executioner Calcraft. The wretched man was attired in the black suit of mourning in which he was apprehended, and in which he appeared at the trial. His arms were firmly strapped, but he walked along with freedom. He was exceedingly pale, and quite changed in appearance from what he was at the trial. In coming up the stair, he looked upwards and moved his lips as if in silent prayer.

On reaching the top of the stair, he advanced to the table in front of the bench; and he turned round and spoke to the Governor as if doubtful what he should do. The Governor told him to stand at the table, when Bailie Brown then asked the prisoner, in an almost inaudible tone, if he had anything to say. The convict then bowed to the magistrates and said in a low tone, 'I acknowledge the justice of the sentence.' He again bowed to the bench, and a short conversation took place as to the proper way to the scaffold.

The procession was then re-formed, the town officers going first, and Pritchard following, with Calcraft immediately behind. The prisoner, before leaving the Court, looked around him, and then, with his face upwards and muttering a prayer, he passed through the lobby into the principal entrance and thence to the scaffold.

As soon as he left the table in the Court, there was a general rush to the door on the part of the spectators, when the captain of the police called out that the order of the procession was that the magistrates should come first, the reporters next, and the others in Court afterwards. However, after the prisoner had got beyond the door of the Court the crowd pushed forward, and the passages were blocked up.

Before the last person who left the Court could reach the front of the Jail, Dr Pritchard was standing on the scaffold with the white cap on his head, and Calcraft adjusting the rope round his neck. He walked firmly up the steps to the scaffold, and stood quite erect while he was being handled by the executioner.

He slightly stumbled on coming to the drop, which he struck against with his foot unwittingly, but he promptly recovered himself, and stood firm, without moving a muscle. When he appeared on the scaffold great commotion prevailed amongst the crowd. Exclamations were heard to proceed from every quarter among which were such expressions as 'How well he looks!' 'He's very pale!' 'That's him!' and 'Hats off!' &c. Mr Oldham read a short written prayer, while Calcraft adjusted the cap, put aside the long hair and beard to allow the rope to be rightly placed, and tied the legs. Calcraft, after putting the rope round the prisoner's neck, and drawing the cap over his face, steadied the wretched man by placing his hands on his back and breast. On a signal being given by the culprit, the bolt was drawn, and at ten minutes past eight o'clock he was launched into eternity.

As soon as he was seen dangling from the rope a loud shriek arose from the crowd, and many turned their heads away from the horrid spectacle. The clergymen accompanied Pritchard to the scaffold, but retired afterwards, and no person was with him when he was hanged by Calcraft. Shortly after the drop had fallen, a large number of spectators quitted the vicinity of the scaffold, many of them being observed to shed tears.

There was no screen put round the scaffold, as at some recent executions, but the body was exposed fully to public view. The convict appeared to suffer a good deal, as he shrugged his shoulders more than half a dozen times, his head shook, the whole body trembled and swung round and round; and it was only after Calcraft went below and pulled the legs that it was brought to stillness. The hands were extended as far as they could reach for the pinioning; and the fingers of the right hand pressed off the glove, which fell to the floor. After the lapse of two or three minutes all was quiet, and justice was avenged.

The conduct of the crowd was very decorous latterly. There was no manifestation of feeling against the prisoner when he appeared on the scaffold, but rather approaching silence. After the first murmur of curiosity had passed, Calcraft, who had a faded rose in his buttonhole, met with a hooting on ascending the scaffold to lower the body.

The body hung till a quarter from nine, when it was lowered so suddenly that the bottom was knocked out of the coffin, which was only a plain, pauper shell. It was soon repaired, and Dr Leishman, in presence of two of the magistrates, having certified the death, the body was taken to the vault below the Courthouse, where the beard and hair were shaved off previous to a cast being taken. The body was interred at one o'clock.

Mr Jekyll and Dr Hyde?

THOMAS M. McDADE

THE SWOPE CASE had a traditional *situs* of a classic tale of murder : a mansion built of dark stone on a fourteen-acre estate in Independence, near Kansas City, Missouri. The house, a three-storeyed affair, stood at the end of a long drive amid trees and plantings. The ground floor, entered by a large hall, contained a dining room, drawing room, music room, library, and two spare bedrooms. The first floor had five bedrooms and a sitting room, and the second had three more bedrooms and a ballroom. The mansion also had a tower-like room. There was lots of dark woodwork and there were some coloured-glass windows.

The place had been built by Logan Swope for his growing family. Logan had come to Kansas City after his brother, Colonel Thomas Swope, had made himself the major real-estate operator in the area and a millionaire. This had come about when the railroads selected the area for the major crossing of the Mississippi River, and Thomas controlled the best sites. When Logan Swope died in 1900, there were seven children living in the house — two boys and five girls.

Upon the death of her husband, Mrs Margaret Swope invited brother-in-law Colonel Thomas to join the family, which he did, occupying a large bedroom on the first floor. He was a tough-minded, hard-drinking individual who had never married. He soon adapted himself to the family group.

At the same time, Mrs Swope also asked a cousin of her deceased husband, Moss Hunton, to join the family.

Hunton, bearded like an Old Testament patriarch, was a quiet, studious man who did not intrude on the others. He kept to a small bedroom on the ground floor.

By 1909, the family was little changed. One daughter, Frances, had married Dr Bennett Clark Hyde despite her mother's objections. Hyde's relations with women had been questionable, but Frances had refused to give him up, and they now lived in a house in Kansas City given to the couple by old Colonel Swope, who did not have the same objections to the doctor as had Mrs Swope. Young Tom Swope, the youngest of Margaret's two sons, had married and lived on a farm not far distant. Mrs Swope herself, now a large-bosomed, fifty-four-year-old, double-chinned dowager, presided over the family, all of whom seemed to get along with one another. Now that she was reconciled to her daughter's marriage to Dr Hyde, that couple frequently visited the family mansion.

Though over eighty, Colonel Swope (the title was honorary) managed his many business interests and made frequent trips to Kansas City. On 9 September 1909, however, he had a fall which injured his shoulder and briefly confined him to his room. A nurse, Pearl Kellar, was obtained to tend him. Dr Hyde, although practising in Kansas City, did not act as the family physician. The nurse, an outgoing, optimistic person, brought the old Colonel around so well that in a couple of weeks he was talking of going into the city again on business.

Meals at the big house seem to have been casual affairs. On 1 October 1909, old Moss Hunton, looking much older than his sixty years, was eating in the ground-floor dining room with Nurse Kellar, Mrs Swope and her daughter Margaret. Hunton suddenly felt faint and said that he had lost control of his right side. The nurse got him to a couch, and, when the family doctor, George T. Twyman, arrived, Hunton was carried into his bedroom. Shortly, Dr Hyde arrived and joined the council. The doctors agreed that Hunton had had an apopleptic stroke, and, when Dr Hyde suggested that he be bled to relieve pressure on the brain,

Twyman assented. There is a dispute as to what was said during the blood-letting. Twyman felt that enough had been drawn and wanted it stopped; Hyde felt that more needed to be taken. When Hyde's wife suggested that he follow Dr Twyman's advice, he closed the opening. When the blood which had been taken was measured, it was found to be two quarts. When the nurse returned to the room after disposing of the blood, Hunton was dead.

Later, Hyde would ask Nurse Kellar to suggest to Colonel Swope that he, Hyde, be named to replace Hunton in Swope's will as executor, but she refused. Old Swope was sad on learning of Hunton's death, as he and his cousin had been close.

The next day, Dr Hyde went with the nurse to see Swope. During the visit, the doctor gave the nurse a capsule 'for Mr Swope's digestion'. The old man would not take it immediately but did a little later, and within twenty minutes the nurse found him staring, his eyes dilated, hands and teeth clenched, his whole body quivering. When Hyde saw Swope, he declared that he had had an attack of apoplexy. At the doctor's direction, the nurse gave Swope a 1/60 grain of strychnine. After much retching and vomiting, the old man became conscious and voiced regret at having taken the medicine.

More injections of strychnine were given to Swope during the day, Nurse Kellar staying with him. When she left briefly for dinner, she returned to find Hyde and his wife there, and she was greeted by Mrs Hyde's statement that 'Uncle Thomas has just gone'. There were now two corpses in the house.

Hunton was buried on the 4th and Colonel Swope on the 6th of October. The latter lay in state in Kansas City where ten thousand reviewed the body. As one of the principal benefactors of the city, having given, *inter alia* more than 1300 acres for a park, great honours were shown him in death.

Early in December, the house was again shaken by illness. First, Margaret Swope fell ill, then twenty-two-year old Chrisman, her eldest son. When Hyde visited the house, he diagnosed Margaret's illness as typhoid. Hyde had complained about the Swopes' water, and kept his own supply of drinking water there. When Margaret's house-guest, Belle Dickson, was stricken, three more nurses were brought in. Though Dr Twyman was in charge, Hyde continued to enter into the cases. Shortly after Hyde had given Chrisman a capsule, the young man's body became rigid and the nurse could not get a pulse. Hyde tried a number of treatments on Chrisman, but the patient died without coming out of his convulsion. He was buried on 8 December. Two days later, his younger sister Sarah was stricken with typhoid, bringing the number of cases of typhoid in the house back to four.

The oldest daughter, Lucy Lee, was in Paris during these episodes, and returned at her mother's request. Hyde went to New York to accompany her home. While he was gone, all the patients improved. A half-hour after Margaret took a capsule from Hyde, however, she had a seizure which the nurses recognised as similar to Chrisman's. Dr Twyman happened to enter the house at this moment and was able to bring Margaret around with his injections.

At this time, the nurses, in a body, refused to stay on the cases under Hyde. One left immediately, and the others agreed to stay only if Dr Twyman were solely in charge. At this point, the Hydes left the house. There was a curious incident that evening, when young Tom Swope saw Hyde drop something on a street pavement and grind it under his foot. Tom retrieved it later, and it proved to be part of a capsule. It was sent to a laboratory for analysis.

All these events had created a vast amount of talk, and rumours were spreading. On 30 December 1909, Chrisman's body was exhumed and his organs sent to Chicago for analysis. On 12 January, an autopsy was performed on Colonel Swope's body. The Kansas City *Journal* began a lead article with the question : 'Was the late Thomas H. Swope, whose benefactions to Kansas City amounted to more than a million and a half dollars, the victim of a scientific plot which had for its aim the elimination of the entire Swope family, by inoculating with typhoid germs, looking to ultimate control of the three million dollar estate?'

When the doctors in Chicago announced that Swope had died of strychnine poisoning, the police authorities took over the case. On 6 March 1910, Dr Hyde was indicted for the murders of Colonel Swope and Chrisman, for the manslaughter of Moss Hunton, and for the poisoning of other members of the household. His wife announced her faith in her husband, and retained Frank P. Walsh, a radical lawyer, to defend him. A rift developed between Mrs Swope and Frances Hyde, who refused to see her mother as long as Margaret would not express confidence in Dr Hyde. The trial was announced for April 1910.

Hyde's trial began in a bleak courtroom that failed to reflect the majesty of the sovereign State of Missouri. The chief prosecutor was James A. Reed, a leader of the state bar and a leading politician. It was an open secret that Mrs Swope had retained him to strengthen the staff prosecutor; also that she had paid for many of the special investigators and other specialists who had helped to prepare the case. Walsh, Hyde's attorney, had succeeded in having the judge rule that the trial would cover only the death of Colonel Swope. He also sought to limit the evidence to that relating to the Colonel's death; the judge ruled, however, that other deaths and alleged poisonings may have been connected with a plan by Hyde to increase his wife's share in the Swope estate, and that therefore they were relevant to the question of motive. One major development favoured Hyde: the week before the trial, Dr Twyman had been operated on for a burst appendix and died thereafter. The state had lost the one witness best qualified to describe the symptoms of all three dead members of the family.

For background, witnesses reported the value of the estate to be almost $3,500,000, of which $1,500,000 was in the residuary estate to be divided among the surviving nephews and nieces. The next couple of weeks were filled by the testimony of the nurses regarding the treatment of the children. Cumulatively, this evidence was bound to be damaging, for each patient that Hyde had visited had got worse following his ministrations. Even more damaging than the nurses' tales was the evidence of Hyde's traffic in poisons. Hugo Brecklein, a druggist with whom Hyde had an account, testified to Hyde's orders for culture media and potassium cyanide capsules. The latter poison Hyde had said he wanted for killing dogs. The druggist had insisted that Hyde call in person at his shop to receive the poison, and cautioned him of the danger of having it in capsule form. Everyone was impressed with the druggist's statement that in twenty-three years of business he had never before put cyanide in capsules.

A bacteriologist, Dr Stewart, testified that Hyde had purchased cultures of diseases from him. These included diphtheria, typhoid, and other infectious bacteria. Stewart had visited Hyde's office in his absence and found that most of the typhoid culture had disappeared. He also related that he had made an inspection of the grounds of the Swope house and found no evidence of typhoid. The day was a disastrous one for Hyde, and it concluded with the judge revoking his bail and committing him to the custody of the sheriff.

Dr Hektoen from Michigan told a grisly tale of the autopsy of Colonel Swope. The body had been frozen solid, and heat had had to be applied to make it accessible. The brain, solid ice, was sawed into slices, and the examiners saw no evidence of a cerebral haemorrhage. The autopsy of Chrisman revealed no natural cause of death. Dr Hektoen's opinion as to the cause of both deaths: some convulsing or paralysing poison. Hektoen was an impressive witness, and Walsh made a long and searching cross-examination with no visible results. A Dr Haines testified to his own toxicological examination of the organs of Chrisman and Colonel Swope. Chrisman's liver and stomach revealed strychnine. Cyanide was present in Swope's liver. Cyanide had also been found in the pieces of the capsule which Tom Swope had gathered from the sidewalk.

It was now May 1910, and the State rested. It was now the turn of the defence. The first witnesses were doctors who had different views on the causes of death. These local medicos seemed provincial after the State's doctors. As usual, the battle of the experts served more to confuse than enlighten. There was much testimony about whether convulsions occurred in typhoid cases, and statistical evidence did not prove conclusive.

After the doctors came Frances, Hyde's wife, who provided a laywoman's view of the events. None of her evidence was impressive; her testimony chiefly concerned remarks made by the nurses.

Dr Hyde followed his wife to the stand, and Walsh skilfully led him through a day's testimony. On the second day, Walsh had him explain his use of cyanide: 'I had used cyanide for a number of years. This time I had used it for a different purpose, to remove nitrate-of-silver stains from my fingers.' Hyde said he ordered it in capsules to preserve its strength. His cross-examination was by Virgil Conkling, the County Prosecutor. On the subject of cyanide, though claiming he had had it for years, Hyde was unable to name a single source in all that time. Conkling harassed the doctor to the point of making it plain that he had no explanation for his so-called years of using it. Hyde claimed that he never gave any member of the family a capsule: in this, he directly contradicted the nurses. When cross-examination ended, Walsh made no effort at redirect; it was apparent that Hyde had no explanation to offer for his interest in cyanide. The State recalled witnesses who testified to Hyde's giving them capsules. The case was winding down, each side having exhausted its supply of witnesses.

Both prosecution and defence were given ten hours for closing speeches. Prosecutor Reed painted a deadly picture by correlating the dates of the patients' attacks and Hyde's visits to the druggist for the cyanide. Walsh spent six and a half hours roving over the whole case, showing a good grasp of all the salient facts. The following day, Reed concluded with a fine summary of the case for the prosecution, and the jury retired.

All the next day, the jury debated the case, while rumours were rife that they stood eight to four for conviction. But a verdict did not come in, and the jury was sent away for the weekend. By this time, both sides expected a split jury and began looking ahead to another trial.

When the court met on Monday morning, everyone was surprised to hear that the jury had reached a verdict. The foreman rose to announce that they found the defendant guilty of murder and had set his punishment at life imprisonment. Hyde dropped into his seat, and Frances, sobbing, threw her arms around him. The press, questioning the jury, found that on the first count the jury had indeed stood eight to four for conviction. The next day, that ratio had changed as the discussion went on, until they were ten to two for guilty. On Sunday, the last two were brought over, and one stated the reason for the verdict: 'Hyde was his own worst enemy. His own testimony convicted him.'

Walsh encouraged his client with thoughts of the appeal. The trial record of 4200 pages — 1,500,000 words — had to be transcribed and printed. Not until February 1911 did the attorneys go to Jefferson City to argue the appeal before the Missouri Supreme Court. The prosecution appeal brief was 479 pages long, and the defendant's hardly less prolix.

Despite the sizeable record, the Court made its decision in two months. It quashed the conviction due to errors in the admission of evidence and ordered a new trial. First, it found error in the evidence of Hunton's death in that Hyde did not know of the provision for Hunton in Colonel Swope's will and therefore had no apparent motive for killing Hunton. It also concluded that there was not sufficient evidence that Hunton's death was due to the bleeding by Hyde. The justices also ruled that the evidence did not establish that Chrisman was in fact poisoned and that it was error for the jury to have considered his case at all. Nor should the evidence of others' illnesses due to typhoid have been admitted, as there was no evidence that Hyde had used germs to make them ill.

The opinion seemed to restrict the prosecution to the death of Colonel Swope, permitting no, or only limited, evidence about the other cases. There was rejoicing in the defence camp; Mrs Hyde drove to the jail in her electric brougham and, after a visit with her husband, went off to buy a new hat. Almost a year before, Frances had said, 'I'll wear this hat until Clark's case is reversed, no matter how bad it gets.' Now a shoddy thing of nondescript colour and faded flowers, she had worn it everywhere. She emerged from a town shop wearing a bright blue one, with a big blue wing thrust out from it.

A new judge, E. E. Porterfield, was named to handle the new trial. The Hydes, fresh from a trip to Colorado, were confident and relaxed, still supported by Walsh and his staff.

The retrial of a murder case is not unlike a second honeymoon. Not only has all the surprise been eliminated from the event, but the air of expectation, the possibility of the unknown occurrence, the mystery of what is to come, is so reduced that the event has an entirely different character.

There were few talesmen who had not read or formed an opinion about the case, and selecting a jury was prolonged. It was 21 November 1911, a month after they began, when Chief Prosecutor Reed rose to make the opening address. (Since the first trial, he had been elected to the United States Senate, but he would not take his seat until the following March.) The case was now confined to the death of Colonel Swope, but there were endless arguments about what evidence was admissible, and the proceedings moved at snail's pace. When it was clear that Hyde did not intend to take the stand in view of his poor performance at the first trial, the prosecution decided to read into evidence all of his previous testimony.

Six weeks after it had begun, the trial had a real crisis. Harry Waldron, one of the jurymen, disappeared from his room at the hotel where the jury was sequestered. While police hunted for him, everyone marked time. Three days later, he returned home, and his wife notified the court. Though he returned to the court, he was in no condition to sit on the jury, and, as there was no provision in those days for an alternate, the judge could only order a mistrial. Six weeks of the court's time had been wasted, but Walsh was delighted. A new trial was set for May 1912.

May came and went. Some of the cast of characters had changed, and no one was anxious to bring the case to court. Floyd Jacobs had succeeded Virgil Conkling as county prosecutor. Hyde, out on bond, had returned to his medical practice; though he may have lacked patients, he had an office. Frances was still not reconciled with her mother and did not visit the house at Independence. Walsh still steered the defence, and, in January 1913, the trial opened in the same ugly courtroom, where twelve days were needed for the examination of prospective jurymen. Reed was back, a prestigious Senator, to open for the prosecution. Again the case was in crisis when a juryman named Higgins became ill in his hotel room with a fever of 102°. Visions of the Waldron episode occurred to all. Higgins was a special problem; he was a Christian Scientist, and there was the delicate problem of advising medical assistance. Higgins himself had confidence in the absent treatment, which he said his father was furnishing from some distant point. He did not improve, however, and was finally dismissed. All parties agreed to accept a substitute, so another talesman was selected to join those who had already served three weeks.

There were new medical witnesses, chiefly for the defence. But, all in all, the case was pretty much as previously heard. On the last day, the crowd was entertained by the presence in its midst of Frank James, brother of the notorious Jesse, and who had himself been tried for murder in Missouri thirty years before and been acquitted.

The jury retired with the case on a Thursday; there was still no decision on the Sunday. When the jury reported a deadlock, with a vote of nine to three for acquittal, the judge declared another mistrial. Hyde, while expressing disappointment at not being acquitted, declared himself ready to keep fighting until he was. Mrs Hyde had already spent $150,000, of which sum Walsh was said to have received one third. Rumour had prosecutor Reed receiving $25,000 from Mrs Swope.

Thereafter, the suit seems to have drifted, with no one anxious to push it. Months passed. The spring of 1915 came, and the prosecution put the case over till the fall. That year, Frances Hyde gave birth to a son, James Logan Hyde. By December 1916, another new prosecutor had inherited the case and appeared to want nothing to do with it. The court warned the parties that the case must go to trial or be dismissed. On 9 April 1917, three days after Congress had declared war on Germany, Judge Porterfield dismissed the indictment against Hyde and the case was over.

It had been seven years, lacking two days, since the first trial began. Hyde expressed regret at the dismissal; he would not have the vindication he sought. He was happy, however, at being a father again, this time of a daughter. Other participants in the case did not fade from public view: Reed served three terms in the United States Senate and achieved national prominence in his battle with President Wilson over the League of Nations; Frank Walsh became active in the Mooney-Billings case, serving for years as a volunteer-counsel to the labour agitators found guilty of a bombing who finally won their freedom from prison in California.

The Hydes ran into domestic difficulties, and Frances sued for divorce in October 1920, obtaining custody of the children. Hyde gave up his medical practice, and in 1934, still a vigorous man at sixty-four, was stricken with cerebral haemorrhage and died while reading a newspaper.

Suddenly at a Nursing Home ...

FENTON BRESLER

THE year was 1969. The man talking to me was a retired Detective Sergeant, William Richardson. We were discussing a trial that had taken place more than thirty years before.

He was describing the two people in the dock: She was a plump, short woman, very sociable at first — but she deteriorated as the case went on.

He was a very nice sort of chap. Got the Military Medal during the First World War, you know. In the same battalion as I was.

Their names: Nurse Dorothea Waddingham and her lover, Ronald Sullivan. On 24 February 1936, they stood their trial at Nottingham's Shire Hall. For murder.

Now, I was in Nottingham discussing that case with people who had been involved in the investigation — and making my own research into a double trial that still retains undertones of sadness and poignancy.

Dorothea Waddingham. What sort of a person was she? Her photographs reveal a calloused, big-nosed face, not the sort of face which one associates with the profession of nurse. Another retired policeman — sprightly ex-Superintendent Percy Ellington — told me: 'She wasn't a real nurse. She looked more like a char to me'.

In fact, Dorothea first picked up her smattering of medical knowledge working as a ward-maid at Burton-on-Trent Infirmary — where she met and married Thomas Leech, a man nearly twice her age.

In 1930, with their three young children, they moved to Nottingham. She was still only thirty, but Leech was by then a chronic invalid, unable to work.

The former ward-maid — now 'Nurse' Waddingham — opened a nursing home for the aged. She met Sullivan. He was good-looking, much nearer her own age — and separated from his wife. He moved in.

In June 1933, Leech died. Soon afterwards, Dorothea, her children — and Sullivan — moved to another nursing home.

She now called herself 'Mrs Sullivan'. A fourth child was born. Sullivan helped run the nursing home: he did odd jobs, swept the floors, ran errands, opened the door to callers.

And one keen winter's afternoon in January 1935, he opened the door to Miss Winifred Blagg, honorary secretary of the County Nursing Association.

She asked if there was room for two new patients: eighty-seven-year-old Mrs Louisa Baguley, frail, with a heart condition, and her spinster daughter, Ada Baguley, who was fifty, grossly overweight, and a helpless cripple.

Since the death of Mrs Baguley's husband, six years earlier, they had lived together. Now the widow could no longer cope. They had some money — about £1600 in cash and shares.

Could Nurse Waddingham take them in?

The answer was: 'Yes'. At that time she had only one patient, an old lady named Mrs Kemp. How much would the Baguleys pay? 'Thirty shillings a week each is all they could afford', said Miss Blagg. It was agreed. A few days later they arrived. And all went well — for a month or so.

Then — '£3 a week for the two of them is not enough,' Nurse Waddingham told Miss Blagg. 'They've got money. If they'll turn it over to me, I'll keep them for life'.

Miss Blagg was horrified. And so were the Baguleys' relatives and solicitor.

But cash was short at the nursing home. Dorothea's only

other patient – old Mrs Kemp – had died. Four adults and four children were living on the Baguleys' £3 a week.

Something had to be done.

Dorothea stepped up the pressure. 'If they don't turn over their money to me, they'll have to go to an institution', she told a visitor. Their solicitor noted that they were deeply concerned at the prospect of being turned out of the home.

So, on 7 May 1935, Ada Baguley made a will. It is a sad document. Ada left all her property to be shared equally by Dorothea and Sullivan 'in consideration that they have undertaken to look after me and my mother for and during our joint lives'.

Within five days Mrs Baguley was dead.

'Cardiac muscular degeneration,' wrote Dr George Herbert H. Manfield on the death certificate. He was the nursing home's regular doctor, but he was not present when Mrs Baguley died.

She was buried. Ada sobbed quietly by the graveside. Then Sullivan wheeled her to the waiting car.

'The relatives can write to Ada,' Dorothea told a cousin, 'but we open all letters, and if they are not approved they are not given to her.' To another visitor she said bluntly: 'We have taken control of Ada.'

But Ada appears to have been happy enough. When Dr Frank Jacob, her old doctor and a family friend, visited her in early August, he found no cause for anxiety.

And when Mrs Alice Briggs, another family friend, visited her on Tuesday afternoon, 10 September 1935, she seemed 'very bright'. Sitting happily in the garden.

Yet by 10 am the next day, four months after Mrs Baguley's death, Ada too was dead. Again Dr Manfield was not present. 'I tried to leave a message, but you were out on your rounds,' Dorothea told him.

What had happened?

Dorothea's version was: 'She wasn't so well yesterday. She had a heavy mid-day meal which seemed to upset her. About two o'clock this morning she was breathing very

223

loudly and slowly. She was very flushed and she was unconscious. Later the colour changed. I thought she was dying and I telephoned you. She was in a coma for about four hours.'

The doctor carried out an external examination, then wrote on the death certificate: 'Cerebral haemorrhage due to cardial vascular degeneration' – in plain English, a stroke. This was consistent with her medical history, her obesity, his examination – and Nurse Waddingham's account of the patient's last hours.

'George Manfield was a nice old boy – but a bit soft, too casual,' a doctor who knew him well has told me.

He trusted Nurse Waddingham. And did not even pause when she produced a letter addressed to him, signed by the dead woman, and dated 29 August 1935, a fortnight before her death:

> I desire to be cremated at my death for health's sake, and it is my wish to remain with the nurse, and my last wish is my relatives shall not know of my death.

It was witnessed: 'R. J. Sullivan.'

Pliantly, Dr Manfield signed a cremation certificate – and got another doctor to countersign it. Next morning, Sullivan presented the papers at Nottingham Crematorium. But Dr Cyril Banks, the crematorium's medical referee, was less easily satisfied than Dr Manfield.

Apart from the letter's strange wording, he noticed that – except for the badly scrawled signature – it all seemed to be in the same handwriting as the witness's : R. J Sullivan.

He informed Wilfred Rothera, the astute Nottingham City Coroner, who ordered an immediate post-mortem examination.

It took place that afternoon. While the two post-mortem doctors worked on the corpse, Dr Manfield watched. He had been asked to attend.

It was too early for a final assessment of cause of death; the organs would have to be analysed. But the two doctors saw at once — and Dr Manfield reluctantly agreed — that Ada Baguley had *not* died of a stroke. The preliminary verdict was: *Death due to failure of her degenerated heart, brought about by pneumonia starting in the lungs.*

But why should Ada — recently sitting in the mid-September sun — have suddenly developed pneumonia?

The analysis of her organs gave the answer. They contained over five grains of morphia. In the case of a chronic invalid such as Ada, that was more than enough to cause a coma — which might well bring on pneumonia.

The post-mortem final verdict: *Death by morphia poisoning.*

The inquest opened. But Nurse Waddingham was 'too ill to give evidence'. In fact, she was in the last months of pregnancy with her fifth child.

A few days later, a detective inspector visited her. 'I have never given Miss Baguley any morphia.' she told him. She said the only morphia she had ever had was for her two previous patients — and she had none left after they died.

What about Ada's strange cremation letter?

'Mr Sullivan made it out at Miss Baguley's request and she signed it,' she said. Sullivan confirmed this.

The police searched the house. They found no morphia.

The investigation had reached a full stop. But on 30 September, Mrs Baguley's body was exhumed. And morphia was found in her body as well.

What was Dorothea's explanation of *that?*

The police could not ask her at once. On 20 October she gave birth to a girl. Several weeks passed before she was well enough for further questioning.

By then she was near-hysterical. She remained so, off and on, throughout the ensuing months.

'I know there is no morphia in Mrs Baguley,' she cried. 'I reckon this is a put-up job. If there is any morphia, somebody might have brought it in. A woman named Rose used to come. I don't know who she is. I noticed Ada used to pay her.' The police checked: there was no 'Rose'.

Sullivan was much calmer. 'To my knowledge there was no morphia kept in Mrs Baguley's room,' he said.

Where had the morphia come from?

Dr Manfield told the police that he had never prescribed it for either mother or daughter — except as a very small part of a harmless pain-killer for Ada. Dorothea raised some wild story about a local chemist possibly having made a mistake — but that did not stand up to investigation. Where *had* it come from?

There was one distinct possibility. Both her previous patients had been prescribed morphia. Manfield — bumbling, honest, but administratively incompetent — had kept no records. It was only Dorothea's word that she had none left after they died.

It was all highly suspicious. But there was very little hard evidence. There could be no arrest — unless a guilty person 'cracked'.

Into this vacuum stepped the man who had started off the whole inquiry with his post-mortem order: City Coroner Wilfred Rothera.

On 15 January 1936, as a blizzard swept Nottingham, he resumed the inquest on Ada Baguley.

Rothera subjected Dr Manfield to an ordeal in the witness box. It lasted nearly eight hours. The doctor's confusion was exposed to public gaze.

For the last twenty minutes he was questioned by William Smith, Dorothea's burly, pugnacious barrister.

But Smith was strangely muted. He seemed to have little ammunition against Dr Manfield. He merely tried to show that Dorothea had accounted for all the morphia prescribed for her two previous patients.

As usual in coroners' courts, most of the questions came from the coroner. Yet, despite four days of Rothera's steely interrogation of nearly thirty witnesses, nothing substantially new emerged — until the moment when he called Dorothea Waddingham into the witness-box.

She could have refused to testify. No one can be forced

to incriminate themselves at a coroner's inquest. But she almost ran into the witness-box. She was so anxious to be heard.

It was a calamitous mistake. And Smith, her counsel, should never have permitted it. 'He fought for her. He fought hard. But he let her down. She should never have given evidence. We would never have been able to pin it on her if she hadn't.' That is ex-Detective Sergeant Richardson talking. There can be no doubt he is right.

In her four and a half hours in the witness-box, Dorothea convicted herself of murder out of her own mouth. It was no 'I did it, I couldn't help it' witness-box confession that occurs in the Perry Mason cases. She vehemently denied her guilt. What sunk her was a single, stupid lie. Her explanation of how the morphia got into Ada Baguley's body.

'I gave it to her!' she said blithely. 'I gave it to her in five separate doses of two tablets each.' Why? Where had it come from? 'Dr Manfield told me to do it. He left me six tablets when he called in August and four more in early September. He told me to give them to her when her pain was bad. I gave her the last two at eight o'clock on the night she died.'

Just look at the appalling stupidity of this statement:

(1) She need not have said *any*thing. No one could then ever have proved that she had administered the morphia.

(2) She had already told the police: 'I have never given Miss Baguley any morphia.'

(3) Dr Manfield had sworn in evidence that he had never prescribed morphia for Ada. Why should he have lied?

(4) When cross-examining Dr Manfield, Smith, her counsel, had not put one word of this sensational accusation. Why not? There was only one possible explanation: because he did not know Dorothea Waddingham was going to make it.

Dorothea could not be controlled. She seemed to lose all sense of discretion. Pressed by Rothera as to why she had said nothing to the police or the court about Ada's morphia tablets, she gave the fantastic reply : 'Dr Manfield told me not to.'

At that point, any lingering belief in her innocence must have departed. Dr Manfield may not have been the most up-to-date doctor in Nottingham. But his integrity was undisputed. A citizen of Nottingham told me : 'It is inconceivable that he could have lied, or told anyone else to do so.'

When eventually Dorothea left the witness-box, the crowded court was hushed. Everyone knew that something frightening and horrible had happened. A woman had put her foot on the scaffold.

The proceedings were not yet completed. What of Sullivan? He declined to give evidence. As with Dorothea, Rothera warned him that he need not testify. 'I don't think it is necessary,' Sullivan said. And left the witness-box.

But the damning effect of Dorothea's testimony engulfed him. The jury's verdict was: *'That Ada Louisa Baguley was murdered by Ronald Joseph Sullivan and Dorothea Nancy Waddingham.'*

As Dorothea screamed, they were both arrested.

The law now acted quickly. It seemed that the authorities wanted to get it over with quickly. They had already waited too long.

There was a police-court hearing. The trial was fixed for only eight days ahead. William Smith applied to the assize judge for more time. A KC was being brought in to lead Nurse Waddingham's defence — 'and he has not even received his brief yet,' said Smith.

But the judge was Mr Justice Goddard — later Lord Chief Justice. The application was refused.

Norman Birkett, KC, prosecuted at the trial. He was his usual suave, effective self. But the case hardly needed his talents. Dorothea was as good as convicted before she went into court.

The only fresh point to emerge was brought out, not by Birkett, but by the judge. After most of the prosecution witnesses had given their evidence, Goddard asked Dr

Frank Jacob, Ada's old doctor, to come back into the witness-box.

'Tell me, doctor,' said Goddard, 'was the deceased at any time when you saw her in such a condition or complaining of any pain such as a doctor would think it right to administer morphia to her?'

The reply: 'She never complained to me at all of any such pain.'

It was crucial. Even if the jury felt that there might just possibly be something in Dorothea's story about Dr Manfield and the morphia tablets, here was a totally independent doctor saying that Ada's condition would not have justified such treatment. There would have been no reason for Dr Manfield to prescribe that dangerous drug.

Yet Goddard was – like many other 'strong' judges – scrupulously fair. Though no one could doubt that he was convinced of Dorothea's guilt, she was not alone in the dock. When Norman Birkett closed the prosecution case, Goddard at once said: 'What evidence do you say there is against the male prisoner? There is no direct evidence against him of possession of morphia. There is no direct evidence against him of administration of morphia.'

Birkett attempted to argue, but the judge was adamant: 'No, Mr Birkett,' he said. 'It seems to me that it amounts to no more than that the prisoner Sullivan *may* have been connected with the matter. Not that he *must* have been.' He ordered Sullivan to be released. At once.

The trial against Dorothea went on. Twenty-four hours later came the inevitable verdict: Guilty. The only surprise was that the jury made a strong recommendation to mercy; perhaps because of her five children.

'I am innocent,' she whispered as she was sentenced to death.

'There is a natural reluctance to hang a woman,' the Home Office once told a Royal Commission on Capital Punishment. But Sir Alexander Maxwell, Permanent Under-Secretary at the Home Office in 1936, told me some years ago, when I was writing a book on the reprieve system, that Sir John Simon — then the Home Secretary — once said to him: 'Don't expect me to reprieve a murderer merely because she is a woman.' And poisoners were almost never reprieved.

Dorothea struggled against death. She lodged an appeal. It was dismissed. She petitioned for a reprieve. It was dismissed. From the death cell, she wrote to Sullivan: 'Now don't be afraid. I shall be all right, don't worry.' On the eve of her execution, she called for her solicitor, and he sent Home Secretary Simon a last-minute telegram, pleading for a respite. It was refused.

At nine o'clock on the morning of Tuesday, 16 April 1936, twelve thousand people congregated outside Winson Green Prison. Traffic was halted. Wealthy abolitionist Mrs Van der Elst harangued the crowd from her Rolls-Royce. Loudspeakers relayed hymns, men bared their heads, women knelt in the roadway.

And inside, Dorothea Waddingham half-walked, was half-dragged, into the execution room.

'Will it hurt?' she asked.

'Don't worry dearie. You won't feel a thing,' they said.

Just like Ada Baguley and her mother.

The sequel is grim. Dorothea's children were separated. For a time, Sullivan remained alone in the deserted nursing home. Then he left.

And Ada's money? Eventually, it was shared equally between Sullivan and Ada's next-of-kin. Dorothea lost her half-share, for the law says that no one may profit by their own crime. Not even after death.

The Janitor's Story

ALBERT BOROWITZ

IF WE ARE TO BELIEVE the Indiana humorist George Ade, patriots can be competitive even about their countrymen's crimes. Ade tells us of the shipboard traveller from Emporia, Kansas, who tartly responds to an Englishman's criticism of violence in the United States by observing that 'there were fewer murders in England because good opportunities were being overlooked'. Of course, quantity has never been synonymous with quality, and the well-behaved British may be forgiven for the belief that their murders, relatively few though they may be, include inimitable cases — from the Brides in the Bath to Ten Rillington Place. But for the most intriguing of these cases, the American patriot would have a worthy rival to put forward — the Harvard Murder Case of 1849.

The Harvard Murder Case is rightly named because most of the cast of characters were Harvard men: the defendant, the victim, the trial judges, counsel on both sides, and twenty-five of the witnesses (including Dr Oliver Wendell Holmes). The defendant, John White Webster, was a professor of chemistry at Harvard University and at the Harvard Medical College in Boston. The victim, Dr George Parkman, was a benefactor of the medical college who drew his wealth from real-estate investment and private moneylending. His generosity as a philanthropist was matched (and probably facilitated) by his relentlessness as a creditor; one of his slow-paying debtors was Webster, who had exhausted what little patience Parkman had by fraudently selling off a mineral collection he had mortgaged as collateral for his borrowing.

On Friday, 23 November 1849, Parkman disappeared. He had stopped off that day at a shop near the medical college to purchase 'a quantity of lettuce, a rare plant at that season,' for an invalid daughter to whom he was much attached, and was last seen alive entering the medical college between half-past one and two o'clock in the afternoon. When Parkman, a man of regular habits, did not return home, his family and friends became alarmed. The next day the police were notified of his disappearance, and a wide search was undertaken. Handbills were issued offering a reward of $3000.

On Sunday, Webster informed Dr Parkman's brother, Francis, that the missing man had called on him by appointment at the medical college at half-past one on Friday and that Webster had settled his debt by paying him $483. The search continued during the course of the following week. Webster's rooms at the medical college were inspected, the river was dredged, and a thorough search was made of the yards, outbuildings, and houses in the western part of Boston, where Dr Parkman had large real-estate investments (and perhaps other defaulting debtors). The police inquiries extended as far as sixty miles throughout adjacent towns.

While the police flailed about without success, an unexpected ally was at work. The janitor of the medical college, Ephraim Littlefield, whose living quarters were adjacent to Webster's laboratory on the upper basement storey of the medical college building, suspected that Parkman's body must be hidden somewhere on the premises and concluded that the only place that had not been inspected was the vault under Webster's privy. On 29 November (the Thursday after the disappearance), he set to work to pierce the privy vault, and on the next day completed a breach of the wall. Inside the vault, near the opening he had made, Littlefield found certain remains of a human body — a pelvis, the right thigh and the left leg from knee to ankle — and some towels marked with Webster's initials and similar to those used by the professor in his laboratory.

On Friday evening and Saturday morning, the police also found in an assay furnace (a furnace used to test metals) in Webster's laboratory, fused with slag and cinders, a great number of fragments of human bones and certain blocks of false teeth. Later on Saturday, they also discovered in a remote corner of the laboratory, in a place they had previously noticed but not examined, a tea-chest that contained, imbedded in a quantity of tanning material and covered with minerals, the thorax of a human body, a left thigh, and Webster's hunting knife. Around the thigh bone was tied a piece of twine similar to that found in one of Webster's drawers. The various remains were examined and found to be parts of a single body that resembled the body of Parkman. Dr Keep, Parkman's dentist, identified the false teeth found in the furnace as part of a set he had prepared for the missing man.

Webster was arrested and charged with the murder of Parkman. From his cell, he accused Littlefield either of committing the murder or of conspiring to fix the guilt on him. Webster was represented at his trial by two well-known members of the Massachusetts Bar, Edward D. Sohier, who had been primarily a civil lawyer, and Pliny Merrick, a judge of the Court of Common Pleas. Merrick had greater criminal experience than Sohier, having served as district attorney, but Sohier took the role of lead counsel, because he had represented Webster in certain matters in the past. After an eleven-day trial, the jury deliberated for a little less than three hours and returned a verdict of Guilty; Webster was sentenced to be hanged. An appeal was made on his behalf to the governor for commutation of the sentence, and in the course of that appeal, in which Webster had initially asserted his innocence, a confession of the murder was ultimately filed with the Committee on Pardons of the Massachusetts Executive Council. That confession was promptly labelled

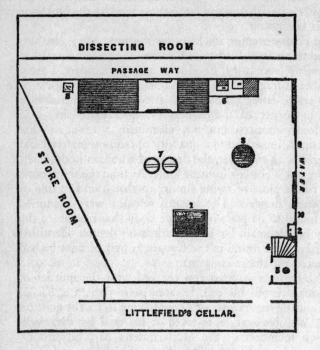

Explanation of the Diagram

1. A wet sink, connecting with the vault by a small pipe.
2. Sink, with Cochituate water.
3. Stove.
4. Staircase leading from the laboratory to the Professor's private rooms, and encircling the privy.
5. Privy, immediately under which the pelvis, right thigh, and lower part of the left leg, were found.
6. Furnace, in which were found the mineral teeth, parts of bones of the head, neck, arms, hands, right leg and feet.
7. Two large casks, for chemical purposes.
8. Tea-chest, in which the thorax and left thigh were discovered.
9. A very large window, overlooking the water, and about two feet above it, at high tide.
10. Another large window, but not so wide as No 9, also overlooking the water. Both windows are without blinds or curtains.

a 'hoax' by much of the press, because it contained some puzzling factual assertions and also was viewed as a last-ditch effort by Webster to save his life. In any event, clemency was denied, and Webster was hanged on 30 August 1850.

Obviously, the key to the case against Webster had been Littlefield's discovery of Parkman's remains, and therefore the centrepiece of the trial was 'the janitor's story'. Although the presiding judge, Chief Justice Shaw, suggested in his charge to the jury that 'the facts and circumstances' that the janitor discovered 'constitute the substance of the evidence', the judge cannot have failed to notice from Littlefield's testimony that his search for the body was oddly motivated and spasmodically performed.

Littlefield testified that he had been employed as janitor of the medical college for seven years and had known the defendant during that period; he had been acquainted with Parkman for twenty years. He was present at an interview between Webster and Parkman on the Monday prior to the disappearance. He heard Parkman ask, 'Dr Webster, are you ready for me tonight?' Webster answered, 'No, I am not ready tonight, Doctor.' Parkman accused Webster of selling or remortgaging collateral, and warned him as he left that 'something must be accomplished tomorrow'. Littlefield also said that, on the same Monday and before Parkman called, Webster had asked him a number of questions about access to the vault under the dissecting room of the medical college. The following day Webster asked Littlefield to carry a note to Parkman.

On Friday morning, 23 November, as Littlefield set his broom behind the door to Webster's back-room off the chemistry lecture-room, he noticed a sledgehammer that was usually kept in the laboratory below. The sledgehammer thereafter permanently disappeared, and Littlefield's recollection of its unusual whereabouts on the fatal Friday appeared to contain a gratuitous suggestion of its possible use as the murder weapon. Other signs of hostility to the defendant are scattered through the janitor's testimony, but in view of the accusations Webster had made against him, the witness's irritation is understandable.

The janitor further stated that on the afternoon of Friday 23 November, shortly before two o'clock, he saw Parkman coming towards the college, 'walking very fast' (a not inappropriate gait for a persistent creditor). Later, when he went downstairs to Webster's laboratory-stairs door, which led out into the janitor's cellar, Littlefield found that door and another door to the laboratory bolted on the inside. He thought that he heard Webster walking inside the laboratory and water running. About half-past five, as he was coming out of his kitchen, he heard someone coming down the back stairs that led into the janitor's cellar. It was Professor Webster, holding a lighted candle.

On Saturday morning, Littlefield unlocked the door of Webster's lecture-room and tried to get into his adjacent back-room, but found it locked. Presently, Webster arrived, a small bundle under his arm, and unlocked the door to the back-room. He asked the janitor to make him up a fire in the stove.

Littlefield testified that on Sunday evening he had a conversation with Webster that aroused great misgivings in him. Webster asked him whether he had seen Parkman during the latter part of the preceding week, and the janitor told him that he had seen him coming towards the college about half-past one on Friday. The professor then volunteered that this was the very time that he had paid Parkman $483 and some odd cents. The janitor was struck with Webster's unusual demeanour: 'Usually, when Dr Webster talks with me, he holds his head up and looks me in the face. At this time, he held his head down, and appeared to be confused, and a good deal agitated. I never saw him so before; that is, look as he did: My attention was attracted to it. I saw his face, and I thought that he looked pale.' On Monday, the janitor tried twice to get into Webster's room to make up his fires but found the doors bolted. On the same day Littlefield was in Webster's laboratory briefly on three occasions while visitors were calling in connection with the Parkman disappearance. The following day, he was present during a police inspection of Webster's rooms; it seemed to him that when one of the police officers, Mr Clapp, inquired about the privy, the professor 'withdrew the attention of the officers from that place'.

On Wednesday morning Littlefield saw Webster arrive at the college early and soon heard him moving things around in his laboratory. The janitor went to the laboratory door, tried unsuccessfully to look through the keyhole, and began to cut a hole in the door but gave up because he thought Webster had heard him. Later that day, as he was passing by, he found that the walls near Webster's laboratory were unusually hot. He thought that the fire must be coming from the assay furnace, where he had never known a fire to be, and was afraid that the building would take fire. He climbed the wall to the double window of the laboratory, found it unfastened, and went in. The first place he inspected was the assay furnace, in which he found only a small fire. He then examined two water hogsheads and found that two-thirds of the water was gone from one and that all the water had been drawn from the other. He also noticed that two-thirds of the pitch-pine kindlings in the laboratory were gone. As he went upstairs, his eye was caught by some spots on the stairs he had never seen before. Putting his finger to them, he found that they tasted like acid.

Thursday was Thanksgiving. In the afternoon, about three o'clock, Littlefield set about digging a hole through the wall of the vault under Professor Webster's privy. He testified in explanation of his action:

> I wanted to get under there to see if anything was there, and to satisfy myself and the public; because whenever I went out of the College, some would say, 'Dr Parkman is in the Medical College, and will be found there, if ever found anywhere'. I never could go out of the building without hearing such remarks. All other parts of the building had been searched, and, if

nothing should be found in the privy, I could convince the public that Dr Parkman had not met with foul play in the College.

Using a hatchet and a chisel, he worked about an hour and a half, but found he could not make much progress with these tools and gave up the job for the night. He went out that night and stayed up till four o'clock the next morning at a ball given by a division of the Sons of Temperance. About noon on Friday, he had a conversation with Dr Henry Bigelow of Harvard. He asked Bigelow whether he knew if there was any suspicion of Webster, and Bigelow told him there was. Littlefield informed Bigelow that he had commenced digging through the wall and understood him to encourage him to continue the work. He testified that he received similar exhortations from Professor John B. S. Jackson. Armed with this moral support from the Harvard faculty, he asked a foundry worker, Leonard Fuller, to lend him a crowbar, hammer, and chisel. He went back to work and made rapid progress. When he broke through the last of the five courses of brick in the privy vault, he made his grisly discovery.

This testimony by Littlefield was a focal point of a withering attack made in the press and within the ranks of the legal profession on the conduct of the Webster trial. The criticism of the trial spared no one: Chief Justice Shaw, the prosecution, and the defence counsel all were subjected to abuse. In fact, the conviction of Webster led to a kind of regional warfare between the bars of New York City and Boston, with several New York lawyers leaping into print anonymously to savage the reputation of New England justice, and their Massachusetts colleagues rising against them in stout defence. One of the published diatribes against the Webster trial that won wide notoriety was a pamphlet entitled *A Review of the Webster Case, by a Member of the New York Bar* (1850). It is now known that the author was A. Oakey Hall, a colourful Harvard Law School graduate whom Tammany Hall was to elect mayor of New York in 1868. By a stroke of luck that often awaits the compulsive bookbuyer, I recently happened upon a scrapbook of Hall's memorabilia of the Webster trial containing his manually annotated copy of a trial report, a group of pamphlets (including his own *Review of the Webster Case*), law-journal articles, and newspaper clippings. These materials provide a unique insight into the roots of Hall's criticism of the trial.

A principal target of Hall's attack was the 'silence and timidity of cross-examination evinced by the counsel for the defence,' each of whom, to his mind, perhaps, 'thought more of playing the polished gentleman than discharging the duty of the enthusiastic advocate; and kept ever in mind that decorum and courtesy were more important than the acquittal of their client'. Hall was particularly sharp in his criticism of deficiencies in the cross-examination of Littlefield. He complained that the defence had not adequately probed the issue of the janitor's access to the scene of the crime. Why did they not press Littlefield about the circumstance that the dissecting room was found unbolted the morning after Parkman's disappearance when it was bolted the night before? And if Littlefield could gain entry into Webster's laboratory on the famous hot Wednesday, could he not have done so on other occasions as well? Hall also argued that Littlefield's 'whole tenor of mind' should have been 'almost minute by minute from Friday to Friday brought into confessional'. Hall's questions pressed on each other: Why had the janitor neglected to investigate the privy earlier? How did he come to hit upon the exact spot in the privy vault where the body would be found? Would he not have found it easier to fit a key to the privy room, unnail the seat and lower a lantern than knock down the wall of the vault?

However, Hall's ultimate criticism was addressed to the failure to mount an all-out attack on Littlefield's credibility: 'Why was not his life raked over from beginning to end; his ways of life investigated that his credibility might be securely known? Were the counsel fearful of a libel suit; or of an assault and battery; or a loss of popularity?'

It is not a simple matter to determine the extent to which Hall's denunciation of defence counsel's handling of Littlefield is justified. Hall probably did not attend the trial and appears to have based his judgments on his reading of an unofficial report of the trial by Dr James W. Stone, which is bound into his scrapbook. Stone's account does not report questions put by counsel, and generally testimony is summarised rather than reproduced verbatim. However, a fair-minded study of even this inadequate record of the Littlefield cross-examination does not fully bear out Hall's charges. The defence's questioning of the janitor, which was handled mostly by Sohier, occupied virtually an entire day of the eleven-day trial. Chief Justice Shaw, in his charge to the jury, observed that Littlefield had been 'much sifted by cross-examination'.

Many of the questions Hall would have like to see pressed seem to have been put by Sohier to the janitor. He dwelt on the apparent inconsistencies in Littlefield's narrative: that he had begun to suspect Webster on the Sunday after Parkman's disappearance; that on the evening of Parkman's disappearance, *even before he entertained such suspicion*, he had returned from a party and tried the door of Webster's laboratory; but that *after he became suspicious of the professor*, he had taken no affirmative steps to investigate until he started to chisel away at the privy vault on the following Thursday. Between Sunday and Thursday, Sohier emphasised, Littlefield had calmly accepted a gift of a Thanksgiving turkey from Webster even though he felt (as he implied in his testimony on direct examination) that this unusual show of generosity was intended to silence him. Moreover, in this same period, he had foregone opportunities to look around Webster's rooms during four visits there in the course of the week after the disappearance, despite the fact that on two of those occasions he was in the company of police officers and at least once thought Webster was trying to distract their attention. On the Wednesday when Littlefield entered the laboratory through a window to determine the source of the unusual heat, he did so only because he 'thought the building was on fire'. He noticed that the assay furnace was pretty hot, but (despite his suspicions) did not uncover the furnace because Dr Webster had told him 'never to touch articles, except placed upon a particular table'. In addition to highlighting the witness's strange reluctance to investigate the premises whose barred doors had previously aroused his apprehensions, Sohier also asked whether Littlefield could not have obtained access to the privy room; and tested the odd coincidence that Littlefield breached the privy vault at the precise spot where the body lay.

But the cross-examination, taken as a whole, still seems unsatisfactory. At least in the summary of the testimony given in the two principal reports of the trial, Sohier does not seem to have probed Littlefield's state of mind and motivation but to have focused instead on the externals of his behaviour, thereby permitting the witness to restate and reinforce the chronological narrative he had given on direct examination. The principal weakness was the failure to make a straightforward attack on Littlefield's credibility.

Littlefield's role in the events at the medical college was, of course, the heart of the problem for the defence. It was certain, as Attorney General Clifford conceded in his closing argument, 'that, these remains being there, it must have been known to Littlefield or Webster'. If the defence were to maintain that the body's presence was unknown to the defendant, they must attribute its deposit (if not the murder itself) to the janitor. But in the cross-examination only two faint jabs were made at the janitor's integrity. Early in his questioning, Sohier (probably attempting to establish a good reason for Webster having bolted his doors) asked Littlefield whether the professer had not caught him in his room at night playing cards. Littlefield made a lame attempt to evade the inquiry. 'I decline answering that question; but I will say that I have not played any cards, in his rooms, this winter.' The only other direct attack on the witness's character was made by co-counsel Merrick, who established at the end of the cross-examination that Littlefield had seen reward advertisements a few days prior to beginning his assault on the privy wall.

However, in 1971 it was revealed by Judge Robert Sullivan, in his *The Disappearance of Dr Parkman*, that defence counsel rejected a more dramatic avenue of attack suggested by Webster in his voluminous trial notes addressed to Sohier. Webster asserted that Littlefield had for years been moonlighting as a 'resurrectionist' (graverobber) and had been supplying dead bodies to the Medical College. The professor theorised that Littlefield had bought Parkman's body in a sack (à la Rigoletto) and attempted to obliterate its identity after he discovered to his horror who it was. Perhaps Sohier and Merrick thought that this suggestion smacked more of melodrama than of evidence. In any event, they let the janitor leave the stand with his story essentially unshaken and without any strong indication as to why he would have murdered Parkman, deposited his body, or attempted to implicate Webster falsely in his death.

Merrick later attempted to plug this gap in the defence — by a lengthy attack on Littlefield in his closing argument. When the bluntness and the biting satire of the argument are compared with the apparent restraint of the cross-examination of Littlefield, it is tempting to speculate as to whether there may not have been a disagreement between Sohier and Merrick on the approach to this key prosecution witness. The possibility of a divergence of views is enhanced by the fact that it was Merrick who intervened towards the end of Sohier's cross-examination to confront Littlefield with the reward handbills and to suggest that they might have motivated his tardy attack on the privy vault. In Oakey Hall's copy of the trial report there are many handwritten marks and angry marginal comments on the Sohier cross-examination, but he made no annotations on the portions of Merrick's closing argument dealing with the janitor's story. Hall's charges of timidity are certainly not borne out by Merrick's onslaught against Littlefield, for Merrick stopped only slightly short of imputing the crime to the janitor.

I regret, Gentlemen, that my duty compels me to allude to the testimony of [Mr Littlefield]. I regret that I am obliged to do so, because I am confident whatever is said about this has a tendency to point a suspicion toward him as the perpetrator of this crime. Now, Gentlemen of the Jury, you must not misunderstand me. I will not take upon myself the fearful responsibility, in defending one man, to charge another with the same crime. Far be it from me to say that I will charge Ephraim Littlefield with this crime! Far be it, whatever may be the tendency of my comments, if the effect should be to fix it upon him — far be it from my intention to connect him with this crime! But, Gentlemen of the Jury, it is my duty to examine, and it is your duty to weigh, the testimony of this witness; and if there be anything which tends to affect the testimony of that witness, you must give it weight, whatever the consequences may be.

In addition to making this strong suggestion of Littlefield's guilt, Merrick attempted to cast a raking light on Littlefield's obscure and conflicting attitudes towards Webster. He noted that, although Littlefield claimed that his suspicions were first aroused by his conversation with Webster on the Sunday after the disappearance, 'you will find that his vigilance anticipated his suspicions, while they were followed by an unaccountable apathy and indifference'. In discussing Littlefield's search of the privy vault, Merrick followed the lines of Sohier's cross-examination by noting how odd it was that Littlefield had not first made any effort to gain access to the privy room itself and how it was even stranger that the remains were found exactly in front of the breach he had made but a few feet from a perpendicular line dropped from the hole in the privy seat. He cast doubt on the prosecution's theory that the remains had been dropped from above: 'Could they possibly have been placed there, in that particular spot, by any efforts through the hole in the privy?'

But his most effective weapon in treating Littlefield's discovery of the remains was the irony with which he

243

recalled Littlefield's inappropriate moods in the course of his grim search. On the first night of his labours the janitor broke off his work 'to join in the amusements of the festival of the season; and, after actually dancing eighteen out of the twenty cotillions that occupied the night, returned to sleep quietly in his bed, in an apartment beneath which, he professes to have believed, were lying the bones of a murdered human being ....' On the following Friday morning, Merrick noted, Littlefield did not rise early to resume his work but chatted pleasantly with Dr Webster, who came into his room at nine o'clock while the janitor was still at breakfast. Merrick pointed out that, when Littlefield decided to obtain from Mr Fuller more effective tools to finish the job, he said in jest that he wanted a crowbar to dig a hole in the wall to let in a waterpipe. Finally, Merrick suggested that Littlefield appeared to take special pains to dismiss all possible witnesses from the scene just before he completed his breach of the privy wall. The defence counsel raised dark suggestions about the significance of this conduct:

> Did not Littlefield too well foreknow the information which he should soon have to communicate? Why else did he rid himself of the presence of all spectators? Why else would he have it that no human eye but his own should look into the vault, until he had first seen these remains there in safe deposit? Were not all things yet ready there for the inspection of others? These are fearful questions, of pregnant suggestion, of momentous import. I leave the answer to your own reflections.

I am left with the impression that Merrick's closing argument was sufficiently effective in its treatment of the janitor that Hall was unjust in passing over it in silence. However, a closing argument can do little to shake the credibility of an opposition witness who has not been successfully discredited on cross-examination. The question then remains why Sohier and Merrick did not make a stronger effort, while Littlefield was on the stand, to raise a substantial question in the jury's mind as to the witness's involvement in the crime or at least in the deposit of the body. By one of the strange quirks of legal history, it is possible that the answer to that riddle is to be found in the influence of another murder case that was tried a decade before in England, the famous Courvoisier case.

A Swiss valet, François Bernard Courvoisier, was charged in 1840 with murdering his master Lord William Russell in his bed in the fashionable Park Lane district of London. On the first day of the trial Courvoisier's counsel, Charles Phillips, sharply cross-examined a housemaid, Sarah Mancer, who had testified against her fellow-servant, Courvoisier. The next morning, prior to the resumption of the trial, Phillips had one of the most chastening experiences a criminal lawyer can have in the midst of a trial: Courvoisier confessed to him that he had committed the murder but in the same breath insisted that Phillips continue the defence. Phillips had a temporary failure of nerve and informed Baron Parke, one of the judges sitting in the case, of his client's confession and requested his advice. Parke was understandably annoyed with Phillips for breaching his client's confidence and prejudicing the judge's position – but, according to Phillips, told him that he was bound to continue the defence 'and to use all fair arguments arising on the evidence'.

On the third day Phillips rose to deliver his closing argument to the jury. The precise words he used on this occasion have been the subject of dispute to this day. It was charged by some, after the news of Courvoisier's confession became public, that Phillips had improperly expressed a belief in his client's innocence. But perhaps a more serious charge was that, despite his knowledge of his client's guilt, Phillips had reinforced his cross-examination of Sarah Mancer by casting a suspicion on her in the closing argument. The latter complaint was to some extent just – although, in his closing speech, Phillips purported to disown his accusations even as he made them:

> I must beg that you will not suppose that I am, in the least degree, seeking to cast the crime upon either of the female servants of the deceased nobleman. It is not at all necessary to my case to do so. I wish not to asperse them. God forbid that any breath of mine should send, tainted into the world, persons perhaps depending for their subsistence upon their character. It is not my duty, nor my interest, nor my policy, to do so.

By chance, the controversy over Phillips's conduct, which raged fiercely immediately after the trial, was rekindled in 1849 when Phillips published a belated justification of his actions. A whole range of ancient questions of professional ethics were faced anew in their most intractable form: Is it appropriate for a trial lawyer to express to a jury his belief in the merits of his client's cause? To what extent should a client's confession, or his counsel's knowledge of or belief in his guilt, restrict the scope of cross-examination or argument? How and where does defence counsel strike a balance between his duty to his client and his obligation not to cause wilful harm to witnesses or third parties?

The revived debate over the ethical issues of the Courvoisier case raised strong echoes in America, and Phillips's courtroom conduct and his subsequent disgrace were very much on the minds of the lawyers in the Webster case and of their critics. It is a reasonable hypothesis that the reluctance of Sohier and Merrick to attack Littlefield more zealously in cross-examination and to brand him in the witness box as grave-robber or murderer was influenced by a desire to avoid Phillips's pitfall. In fact, the controversy over Phillips's professional ethics was explicitly referred to by Attorney General Clifford in his closing argument: he alluded to 'the great case of Courvoisier, for the murder of his master, Lord William Russell – that case which has made all Europe ring with strictures upon the conduct of the Counsel, whether just or unjust'. Lawyers who deplored the performance of Webster's defence counsel cited the example of Phillips's

ggressiveness amid extreme difficulties as a standard by
which Sohier and Merrick must be found wanting. Hall's
approval of Phillips's tactics is evidenced by his inclusion
in his scrapbook of an article favourable to Phillips. But
voices from the Massachusetts bar were heard on the other
side of the question. Hall also placed in his scrapbook an
article on the Webster case from a Massachusetts journal,
the *Monthly Law Reporter*, which, after referring to the
renewed uproar over Phillips in the English press,
commented:

> *Had Dr Webster's counsel adopted the tactics of the
> English barrister, they might have saved their client*; nor
> do we believe that the world would have regarded
> them with less favour on that account. So wanton and
> unreasonable is that fickle despot, public opinion! For
> the honour of our bar, we are glad that they did no
> such thing, and all the lampooners of New York and
> Philadelphia cannot harm them.

Significantly, Hall underlined only the words that are
italicised, the words suggesting a lost opportunity to save
Webster from the gallows.

There is something to be said for Hall's selective reading
of this passage. The ethical problem faced by Webster's
counsel was far different from the dilemma that confronted
Charles Phillips when he delivered his final argument for
Courvoisier. In weighing their duty to provide a vigorous
defence of Webster against their responsibility not to inflict
unnecessary harm on a possibly innocent prosecution
witness, Sohier and Merrick did not have their consciences
burdened with a client's confession. On the contrary,
Webster had himself publicly and privately suggested
Littlefield's responsibility for the crime. Moreover, the
Webster murder case, unlike the Courvoisier case and
perhaps most other criminal trials where guilt has been
imputed by the defence to third parties, involved a crime
whose physical setting made it reasonably certain that
either the defendant or a specific third party (Littlefield)
was responsible for the victim's murder or the deposit of

his remains. Under these circumstances, the failure of Sohier and Merrick to make an all-out attack on Littlefield in cross-examination could well have been interpreted by the jury as a show of embarrassment with their defence. No evidence of guilt can be more devastating in the eyes of a jury than the uneasiness of defence counsel with their client's cause. In this respect, Sohier and Merrick, while doubtless undeserving of the full measure of Hall's abuse, may have failed to serve Webster adequately.

The witnesses who faced the cross-examination of Charles Phillips and of Webster's lawyers were heard of again after the trials in which they had figured passed into history. Sarah Mancer paid a terrible price for her innocent involvement in the Courvoisier case. The *Examiner* of London reported of her: 'The cloud was heavy over her, and it passed so slowly that her life never more escaped from it. She died in a madhouse, driven mad by the sufferings and terrors ... the persecutions ... the harassing interrogations to which she was subjected preceding the providential discovery of the guilt of Courvoisier ....' But Littlefield was clearly made of sterner stuff. A press clipping included in Hall's scrapbook discloses that when an exhibition of waxwork figures of Parkman and Webster opened at Clinton Hall in New York City, 'together with a perfect Model of the Medical College, Boston, in which the lamentable tragedy occurred,' the celebrated janitor appeared as hired lecturer 'to explain to the audience the particulars of the whole affair'.

The New York newspaper commentary was scathing. But one report spared Littlefield so that points could be scored against the arch-enemy Boston. Littlefield, readers were told, was 'not quite so shameless a fellow as we deemed him to be'. After reading the comments of the Sunday press on his announced exhibition, he 'had the grace to pack up his disgusting "traps" and make himself scarce as quickly as possible'. The newspaper gave him credit for a sense of shame and wished him better profit from his regular profession at the Harvard Medical College. With a salvo of local pride that echoed the line of defence Webster had wished his counsel to take, the writer concluded, 'There is a greater demand for dissecting subjects in the Massachusetts medical colleges than for disgusting subjects in New York.'

Postscript

From the *Boston Evening Transcript*, 30 August 1850:

> During a great part of yesterday Professor Webster occupied himself with setting aside little memorials for a few of his friends. He seemed to take much interest in this occupation. He ate a little fresh fruit during the day and exhibited little or no nervousness or physical agitation. Those who have conversed with him of late have felt little apprehension as to his committing suicide. He was evidently fully impressed with a sense that it was the crime and not the gallows that made the shame.
>
> Quite a number of applications have been made to see the prisoner during the last two weeks. Clergymen from various parts of the country have sought interviews and he has received numerous letters of an admonitory or consoling nature. The interview he has, in most instances, declined. The letters he has read. Indeed, throughout his imprisonment, he has kept up his interest in outward affairs, although his thoughts have seemed to be mainly devoted to studies and meditations appropriate to his situation.
>
> The last interview of Dr Putnam, his spiritual adviser, took place between half-past seven and nine o'clock last evening. Of this interview we cannot say much but there was no confession contradictory of that already made by the prisoner. Professor Webster declared himself willing to die on the gallows as 'a partial expiation of the great wrong he had done to society'. He retired a little past twelve and was in a sound sleep a little before one o'clock.
>
> At dusk the first wagon entered the jailyard loaded with stakes and other fixtures required for marking

the ground and erecting the scaffold. Soon after sunrise the gallows was erected in the yard of the jail and every blow struck by the workmen smote on the ear of the prisoner and must have affected him unutterably, although he had prepared himself by anticipation for the dreadful sound. A crowd hung about the jail yesterday afternoon, among them several females, to obtain a sight of the grief-stricken family, but in this they were disappointed. The number of tickets issued for the admission of witnesses within the jailyard was about two hundred and fifty.

Professor Webster slept until six o'clock and awoke calm and refreshed. He ate a hearty breakfast, drank two mugs of tea, smoked a cigar and passed the balance of his supply of cigars to the officers in attendance, with whom he conversed cheerfully and freely. At quarter of eight Dr Putnam and Mr Andrews, the jailer, visited the prisoner in his cell. The arrangements for the execution had all been explained the previous evening and Dr Putnam continued in the cell until the prisoner was taken to the gallows. The gallows was surrounded by some one hundred and fifty persons, including several sheriffs and deputies from abroad and a large police force, but only a few members of the bar or the medical profession were present. The windows of the surrounding houses were crowded by persons of both sexes and all ages, and the tops of the adjacent houses, sheds, outhouses and every available point of view were occupied.

At twenty-five minutes past nine o'clock, Sheriff Eveleth and his deputies mounted the steps of the scaffold and were followed by the prisoner, supported by Dr Putnam, Jailer Andrews and a turnkey. The prisoner took his stand on the trapdoor or drop and immediately under the rope which descended from the top of the gallows frame. He was dressed in a black frock coat, buttoned up in front, black pants and shoes, without any neckcloth and only a portion of the shirt front visible. He entered into conversation with his spiritual adviser, which he continued as long as practical and with apparent calmness and composure.

Deputy Sheriff Coburn called the attention of the witnesses to the reading of the death warrant, which was next done in an audible manner by the sheriff, who with his officers and the assembly, with the exception of the prisoner, remained with uncovered heads during the reading. There was some slight disturbance in the crowd at this time and the reading of the warrant was interrupted by shouts and the crowding of those solicitous to see the appalling spectacle.

The prisoner was then seated while Mr Andrews proceeded to confine his elbows by a strap which also passed around the body and tied the hands crosswise in front. Another strap was bound around the legs just above the knees. After the prisoner had again risen upon his feet the rope was drawn down and adjusted around his neck. The knot was placed a little behind the right ear and the rope being drawn a little too closely the culprit's countenance became flushed and his eyes filled with tears, when the noose was instantly slackened. The black cap was drawn over his head, thus shutting out the beautiful sunlight and blue sky of the fair summer day. The flushed appearance of the prisoner's face continued as the cap was descending, and to the last moment he turned his eyes to Dr Putnam, who stood on the left, leaning upon the railing and much affected.

Sheriff Eveleth announced that in the name of the Commonwealth he would now proceed to carry into effect the sentence of the law. As he placed his foot on the trigger of the drop, the prisoner fell some seven-and-a-half feet and his mortal career was at an end. The body swayed slightly to and fro and in a few seconds after the fall there was a spasmodic drawing up of the legs, but beyond this there was no observable struggle, nor was there any subsequent agitation or quivering of the body.

After hanging thirty minutes the body was examined by Dr Henry C. Clark, city physician, and

Dr Charles H. Stedman of the Lunatic Hospital, and they informed the sheriff that life was extinct. The sheriff then announced the fact to the assembly and after thanking the witnesses for their attendance he dismissed them from further service. The body was taken in charge by John Peak, undertaker, placed in a black coffin, and conveyed to the cell recently occupied by the prisoner.

Acknowledgments and Sources

IN ADDITION to those given in the text: 'The Jigsaw Murder Case', which first appeared in the *Manchester Evening News*, is published by permission of the author; 'The Wives of Dr Bowers' is from *Famous American Poison Mysteries* (Hurst & Blackett, London, 1927); 'Poison of One Kind or Another' is from *Famous Poison Trials* (Collins, London, 1923); 'The Murder of Marilyn' is published by permission of the author; 'The Fatal Gambles of William Palmer' is from *Memories of Famous Trials* (Sisley's, London, 1907); 'The Smethurst Case', from *Victorian Studies in Scarlet* (London, 1970), is published by permission of the author and J.M. Dent & Sons Ltd; 'Dentist in the Chair' is published by permission of the author; 'Murder for Lust of Killing', from *Murder and Its Motives* (Harrap, London, 1952), is published by permission of Joanna Colenbrander, for the Harwood Will Trust; 'Doctor Satan', from *Bluebeard and After: Three Decades of Murder in France* (Peter Owen, London, 1972), is published by permission of Margaret Heppenstall; 'The Polite Doctor Pritchard' is from *Murder and Murder Trials 1812–1912* (Constable, London, 1932); 'Suddenly at a Nursing Home . . .', which first appeared in the *Sunday Express*, is published by permission of the author; 'Mr Jekyll and Dr Hyde?', which first appeared in *The Armchair Detective* (USA), is published by permission of the author; 'The Janitor's Story', from *A Gallery of Sinister Perspectives* (Kent State University Press, USA, 1982), is published by permission of the author.

THE ART OF MURDER

Jonathan Goodman

The world of the arts is rich in allusions to death. Its
image has obsessed painters through the ages, literature
abounds with poison-pen letters and murder plots, and
deathly hushes haunt the theatre while murderous villains
stalk the stage. Sometimes chilling, sometimes killingly
funny, this talk of death can also be a grisly foretaste of
things to come . . .

The thirteen true-crime stories collected here are cases in
point: they are all murders connected with the arts, either
through the victim, the murderer or the circumstance.

Included are some of the most sensational stories of
modern times: the grisly murder of playwright Joe Orton
by his lover Kenneth Halliwell; the shooting of the
famous architect Stanford White in the middle of a first
night performance; the shocking murder by the painter
Richard Dadd of his father, and Oscar Wilde's biography
of Thomas Griffiths Wainewright, poet, painter,
dilettante, forger and poisoner. Here too is an account of
one of the most enduring mysteries of the musical world –
the death of Mozart. Was it by natural causes, by Salieri's
poison, or by something altogether more sinister . . .?

TRUE CRIME
0 7474 0676 6

THE LADY KILLERS

Jonathan Goodman

The firing of a dainty pistol; the administering of subtle poison; quiet, suspicious deaths in the peaceful countryside. They could be elegant mysteries by Agatha Christie. They're not. They're true stories of famous women murderers – suggesting that the female of the species is deadlier than the male . . .

In *The Lady Killers* Jonathan Goodman has gathered together a fascinating collection of true tales of murderesses past and present. They include poisoner supreme Mary Elizabeth Wilson, Euphrasie Mercier, a ladies' companion who brutally murdered her mistress, Alice Crimmins the suspected child killer, and Jean Harris, notorious for her part in the Scarsdale doctor murder case.

So much for the theory of 'the gentle sex': *The Lady Killers* will chill all devotees of true crime with its thirteen tales of passion, domestic tragedy and pure cold-blooded murder . . .

THE CRIMINAL HAND
An Analysis of Criminal Handwriting
Patricia Marne

Handwriting, like a fingerprint, is unique to its owner. And when that owner is a suspected thief, murderer, psychopath or spy, an examination of handwriting can reap more rewards than hours of endless questioning.

It is now widely accepted that handwriting experts – or graphologists – can provide invaluable help in criminal investigations, and they have been instrumental in revealing criminal or anti-social tendencies of men and women in notorious cases – most notably in the 'Yorkshire Ripper' investigation.

In this fascinating study, renowned expert Patricia Marne studies the handwriting of a gallery of rogues, murderers and thieves. From Dr Crippen to Adolf Hitler, Kim Philby to Myra Hindley, 'Jack the Ripper' to Peter Sutcliffe, she examines the clues left by a large cast of characters, revealing the hidden personalities that drove them to crime.

UNNATURAL DEATH
Confessions of a Forensic Pathologist

Michael Baden M.D. with *Judith Adler Hennessee*

John F. Kennedy's autopsy failed to disclose crucial evidence

The deaths of John Belushi and Elvis Presley were far more complex than anyone has let on

Decisive medical findings in the Von Bulow affair were consistently overlooked

These are just three of the shocking revelations in Dr Michael Baden's first-person, no-holds-barred account of his distinguished career in forensic pathology. Formerly the Chief Medical Examiner for the City of New York, he was responsible for determining the causes of tens of thousands of deaths, from those of presidents and rock stars to victims of serial killings, perverted sex rituals, mass disasters, infanticide and drug abuse. In this compelling and often gruesome exposé, he produces dramatic evidence to demonstrate that political intrigue, nepotism and professional incompetence have led to major miscarriages of justice where murder is concerned.

THE CONFESSIONS OF HENRY LEE LUCAS

Mike Cox

Henry Lee Lucas was schooled in sexual deviance by an abusive mother. He soon derived twisted pleasure from torturing farm animals, then savagely slaying them. At the age of twenty-four, his lust for killing led him to take his first human life . . . his mother's.

Partnered by another psychopath named Ottis Toole, Lucas then embarked on an orgy of random killing, leaving in his wake a death toll so staggering that the actual number of his victims may never be known. What is known is that his victims were brutally murdered, sexually assaulted – and then hacked to pieces.

Henry Lee Lucas is currently awaiting his own end on Death Row, having confessed to a staggering 360 murders. His story has entered tabloid folklore all over the world, and inspired the controversial film, HENRY: PORTRAIT OF A SERIAL KILLER. Yet, until now, the whole story has not been documented. After years of research and intensive interviews with Lucas himself, and without flinching from the macabre details, Mike Cox explores the depraved mind of a monster, exposes a life possessed by evil and a horrifying American odyssey of death.

THE FIRESIDE BOOK
OF DEATH
Robert Wilkins

Filled with bizarre and irreverent anecdotes and copiously
illustrated with grisly images, *The Fireside Book of Death*
confronts our deepest-rooted fear.

Psychiatrist Robert Wilkins concentrates unashamedly on
the macabre aspects of death – and records the lengths to
which men and women have gone to cope with such fears
as premature burial, posthumous indignity and bodily
disintegration. In a gruesome selection he tells of Emma,
Countess of Mount Edgcumbe, who while lying in state in
the family chapel awoke to find a sexton stealing her
rings; of Count Karnice-Karnicki's remarkable
contraption, which would sound sirens and flash lights if a
'corpse' was to stir within its coffin; of embalming,
mummification, necrophilia and grave-robbing . . .

Modern medicine has made death remote from our
everyday experience. Yet, perhaps for this very reason, we
remain acutely conscious of our own mortality, and the
physical aspects of death still arouse feelings of enormous
unease. Written with black humour and an eye for the
offbeat, *The Fireside Book of Death* will serve as the perfect
antidote.

"An extraordinary book on the 'theatre' of death"
SUNDAY EXPRESS

"A fascinating book – absolutely the last word on the final taboo"
YORKSHIRE EVENING POST

THE GHOST NOW STANDING ON PLATFORM ONE

Edited by Richard Peyton

More than any other form of transport, the railway has attracted ghosts. For more than a hundred years tales have been told of ghost trains, haunted stations, phantom railwaymen and unearthly passengers. Even with the coming of high-speed diesel locomotives and underground railways criss-crossing major cities, the legends have continued in both fact and fiction.

Historical records include numerous accounts of these phantoms, and in turn have inspired a whole genre of fictional tales, from the strange to the horrific, written by the world's greatest story-tellers. Ranging from Rudyard Kipling and F. Scott Fitzgerald to Ray Bradbury and John Wyndham, some of the best of these have been gathered together in this unique collection, intermingled with factual accounts of railway hauntings on both sides of the Atlantic.

This feast of the supernatural offers hours of spooky enjoyment. And, after reading it, no railway journey will ever seem quite the same again.

IF YOU REALLY LOVED ME

Ann Rule

Just before dawn on 19 March 1985, in a quiet Californian suburb, 23-year-old Linda Marie Brown died a most unquiet death. Beautiful and blonde, the wife of a millionaire, she was the woman who had everything. And yet someone fired two bullets between her breasts as she slept in her bed. The cruel crime seemed to offer no rational explanation. The only two people in the house were Linda's 17-year-old sister, Patti Bailey, and her 14-year-old stepdaughter Cinnamon Brown. David Brown, Linda's husband, who was absent at the time of the murder, wept bitter tears when told he had lost the woman he loved. Detectives questioned all three, and one was convicted of the crime.

But for veteran investigators Fred McLean and Jay Newell, hard questions had gone unanswered. Who had wanted Linda Brown dead? And why? As they disentangled lies from truth, they found that Linda Brown had lived in a world of perverse love and dark secrets, hidden behind a blandly normal facade. They unearthed proof of greed, lust and unimaginable mind games.

And at length their investigation resulted in arrests. In gripping courtroom testimony, the terrible truth behind Linda Brown's murder finally emerged . . .

"An absolute masterpiece of reporting. This is Ann Rule at the top of her game – meticulous, precise and bone-chilling" *Edna Buchanan*

"Ann Rule is the undisputed master crime writer of the eighties and nineties – no one does it better" *John Saul*, author of Second Child

Warner now offers an exciting range of quality titles by both established and new authors. All of the books in this series are available from:
Little, Brown and Company (UK) Limited,
Cash Sales Department,
P.O. Box 11,
Falmouth,
Cornwall TR10 9EN.

Alternatively you may fax your order to the above address. Fax No. 0326 376423.

Payments can be made as follows: Cheque, postal order (payable to Little, Brown and Company) or by credit cards, Visa/Access. Do not send cash or currency. UK customers: and B.F.P.O.: please send a cheque or postal order (no currency) and allow £1.00 for postage and packing for the first book, plus 50p for the second book, plus 30p for each additional book up to a maximum charge of £3.00 (7 books plus).

Overseas customers including Ireland, please allow £2.00 for postage and packing for the first book, plus £1.00 for the second book, plus 50p for each additional book.

NAME (Block Letters) ....

ADDRESS...

....

☐ I enclose my remittance for _____

☐ I wish to pay by Access/Visa Card

Number ⬚⬚⬚⬚⬚⬚⬚⬚⬚⬚⬚⬚⬚⬚⬚⬚⬚⬚

Card Expiry Date ⬚⬚⬚⬚